SEX DRIVE

The Complete Programme for Revitalising Your Sex Life

Also by Donald Norfolk

Fit For Life
The Habits of Health
Think Well, Feel Great
Farewell to Fatigue
Executive Stress
Conquering Back Pain

SEX DRIVE

The Complete Programme for Revitalising Your Sex Life

Donald Norfolk

HEADLINE

First published in 1994
by HEADLINE BOOK PUBLISHING

10 9 8 7 6 5 4 3 2 1

British Library Cataloguing in Publication Data

Norfolk, Donald
Sex Drive
I. Title
613.9

ISBN 0-7472-0932-4

Typeset by
Letterpart Limited, Reigate, Surrey

Printed and bound in Great Britain by
Mackays of Chatham PLC, Chatham, Kent

HEADLINE BOOK PUBLISHING
A division of Hodder Headline PLC
Headline House
79 Great Titchfield Street
London W1P 7FN

Contents

One	Begin the Beguine	1
Two	The Power of Love	11
Three	Two Sleepy People	19
Four	Let Yourself Go	28
Five	Give Me Five Minutes More	40
Six	Enjoy Yourself, It's Later Than You Think	49
Seven	Soft Lights and Sweet Music	59
Eight	Sometimes When We Touch	67
Nine	Sweet and Lovely	78
Ten	I Only Have Eyes for You	89
Eleven	They're Playing Our Song	98
Twelve	Blaze Away	107
Thirteen	Ready, Willing and Able	114
Fourteen	Fit as a Fiddle and Ready for Love	121
Fifteen	Doing What Comes Naturally	130
Sixteen	Love Potion Number Nine	140
Seventeen	Tea for Two	152
Eighteen	For Every Man There's a Woman	172
Nineteen	Our Love is Here to Stay	185
	Notes	198
	Libido Quotient Questionnaire	208
	Useful Addresses	210
	Index	212

Acknowledgements

Writing a book appears to be a solitary pursuit. This is illusory, certainly in the case of a work of non-fiction such as this, which has been produced by a vast team of unseen helpers whose names do not appear on the title page. When a book is launched an author attracts whatever plaudits are bestowed, rather like the winner of a regatta race for single sculls. But authors and oarsmen only do the paddling; others build the boat. My thanks are therefore due to my guardian angels at MBA Literary Agents – Diana Tyler and Ruth Needham – who have got me to the water and given me constant encouragement from the towpath. Great tribute is also due to my editors at Headline – Anna Powell and Lorraine Jerram – who have taken my rough, prototype craft and honed and streamlined it until it was ready for public display. And finally I wish to acknowledge the steadfast support I have received from my wife in this, as in every other venture of my life. Together we hope we have created a book you will appreciate and enjoy.

One

Begin the Beguine

Bats do it, bees do it, even monkeys up in trees do it. Why don't *we* do it? Why is it that in a world throbbing with sexual energy we, the self-acclaimed lords of creation, are so often bereft of sexual enthusiasm and drive? Are we too tired? Is there something lacking in our diet? Are we so busy acquiring material wealth that we have no time for the priceless treasures of life – intimate friendships, carefree play, laughter, leisure and love?

Every generation suffers sexual problems, which are partly a by-product of the culture in which it lives. Forty years ago, when I started in practice, many of my patients were suffering the frustrations of unsatisfied desire. This was a hangover from the Victorian moral code which encouraged a compulsive denial of sex.

Now our mores have changed. Sex today has become a compulsive obsession. Decades after the publication of the Kinsey Report my patients are still suffering sexual hang-ups. But the frustration they most commonly report now is not a dearth of erotic opportunity, but a depressing lack of personal libido. 'When I get home in the evening I am too exhausted to make love,' is a common gripe. This lassitude affects a high proportion of adults, according to a survey I carried out for *Chief Executive* magazine, which revealed that nearly one in every three senior managers in Britain is too tired at the end of the working day to make love.[1] People caught in this trap feel guilty because they are short-changing their partners. As one wife confessed: 'I feel wretched because I know I'm cheating my husband by refusing him sex even when I know he's obviously randy.'

These laments are symptomatic of disorders of desire, which as a group are now the commonest sexual disorders doctors have to treat. The syndrome – which masquerades under such names as hypoactive sexual desire, reduced libido, erotopenia and inhibited sexual desire – has become one of the major epidemics of our age; a leading cause of sickness, depression and marital breakdown. You'll get some idea of the strength of *your* sex drive by completing the questionnaire at the back of this book (page 208).

Professor Raul Schiavi, Director of the Human Sexuality Program at the Mount Sinai Hospital, New York, reports that hypoactive sexual desire is now the 'most prevalent sexual dysfunction in women'.[2] The disorder is equally common in men, among whom it can provoke a sad decline in potency and self-esteem.

Many thousands of patients have visited the Detroit clinic of the world-famous Kinsey Institute for Research in Sex, Gender and Reproduction. Their chief concerns have not been specific sexual problems, like premature ejaculation and vaginal dryness, but sexual 'frequency and interest'.[3] The common queries they raised were: 'Why have I lost my interest in sex?' 'What has happened to my sex drive?' 'Why am I so much less sexy than my partner/girlfriend/husband/wife?'

Medicine is not particularly good at answering these questions. Doctors often know more about tropical diseases, which they may never meet in a lifetime of practice, than about everyday sexual problems. You'll probably find them more helpful if you're suffering from *Leishmania tropica* than if your troubles stem from lost libido. For some strange reason medical students have been found to be more ignorant of sexual matters than students following other courses of academic study.[4] This ignorance is not necessarily dispelled during their medical training, which frequently offers no tuition in psychosexual counselling. This leaves them ill prepared for handling their patients' intimate problems and concerns.

What happens then to people whose sexual get-up-and-go has got up and gone? The vast majority appear to reconcile themselves to their fate. Some seek the help of counsellors, specially trained in sex therapy (see page 210). Many write letters to agony aunts. Others become compulsive readers of sex manuals and the how-to-do-it articles in the glossy magazines. These can be self-defeating, encouraging anxious introspection which destroys carefree, spontaneous love-making. As a humorist remarked: 'Impotence comes from reading too many issues of *Cosmopolitan*.'

The awful truth is that lack of libido has been allowed to develop into a major contemporary scourge, not because it is *untreatable*, but because it is so often allowed to go *untreated*. Sex drive is an inherent power within us all, which we can harness to enrich and empower our lives. This book shows how this can be done, using methods which are simple, natural and highly effective. But is there really a need for *another* sex book?

Where Do I Begin?

In recent years there has been a plethora of sex manuals, telling us more than we ever need, or probably want, to know about sexual anatomy and physiology. We have been led to believe that this publication explosion will bring about a sexual revolution. The conscientious reader of these tomes will now be aware that the average vagina varies in length from 3 to 5 inches. He or she will also know that for 40 per cent of American couples the sex act lasts for less than five minutes. This is fascinating information, but has it really 'revolutionised' our lives?

Most well-read adults today could answer questions about clitoral stimulation and cunnilingus which would have been meaningless to their parents. But are they any happier as a result? Now that we are *au fait* with foreskins and foreplay are we enjoying richer, fuller, more exhilarating sex lives? Psychoanalyst Eric Fromm thinks not. 'It often occurs to me,' he conjectures, 'that there is an inverse relationship between the number of books perused by a person or rolling off the presses in a society and the amount of sexual passion or even pleasure experienced by the person involved.'

This paradox is easily explained. We achieve our full, erotic potential, not in an atmosphere of critical introspection, but in an environment of abandonment and total spontaneity. Sexual desire is not a mystery to be solved, it is a gift to be experienced and enjoyed. How can we lose ourselves in the act of love when we are struggling to find our way through the scientific labyrinths of erogenous zones, G-spots and clitoral sheaths? In matters of sickness and health, ignorance is some-times not only bliss, but also therapeutic. The sexologists have helped us break the chains of Victorian ignorance and taboo, but we have replaced them with the fetters of 'performance anxiety'. In the old days our only yardstick of sexual performance was what we did ourselves. Anyone who was less active was frigid; anyone who did it more was a raving sex maniac.

Now we have national norms and averages which we use to set hard and fast performance targets. We want to keep up with the Joneses. If they do it three times a week, we want to do the same. If our neighbours are experimenting with SM, troilism or coitus-a-tergo we feel we are failing if we do not follow suit. These goals are as rigid, demanding and dull as industrial output targets. We have become sexual Stakhanovites, desperately anxious to achieve the national norms. Every time we make love we expect to achieve a mighty orgasm which will convulse our bodies with all the fury of a *grand mal* seizure. These unrealistic expectations are making an onerous duty of what should be an effortless delight.

Sex has become dehumanised. We have become robots, going through the motions, but failing to enjoy the emotions. The multitude of sex books has left us wiser, but little happier. Often they have made us perplexed, a bewilderment well expressed by Woody Allen, who complained: 'I finally had an orgasm . . . and my doctor told me it was the wrong kind.'

How Little We Know

Human sexuality is basically triphasic. It begins with a stage of desire, proceeds through a period of mounting arousal, and culminates in a stage of orgasm. At present we gloss over the initial phase, and focus our entire attention on the final stages of foreplay, petting, coupling and climax. This is where the drama lies; this is where we get our titillation and erotic thrills. But sex without desire is like a whoopee cushion without air.

Sex education today is putting the mechanical cart before the motivational horse. Its prime interest is in genital anatomy, sexual pathology and erotic calisthenics. It is treating sex as if it were no more meaningful than squeezing a blackhead or clearing an ear of wax. This approach is doomed to failure, being little better than setting out to teach the skills of *bel canto* by singing to people who have neither love nor ear for music. There is a wise old saw – 'Where there's a will there's a way' – which should warn us of this danger. We are offering a detailed description of the *way* to people who may often lack the *will*.

Sexual energy is the well-spring of life. With it we have empathy, warmth, confidence, charisma and youthful vitality. Without it we feel lifeless and dull. An unwanted loss of libido can ruin our lives, and yet it is one of the least understood and most poorly treated of all modern diseases.

Nice 'n' Easy

It's a cruel trick of nature that the things we most desire are invariably the most elusive. The harder we try to sleep, the wider awake we become. When a man worries about his ability to have an erection, he increases his risk of being impotent. In the same way when a woman is

4

over-anxious to reach a climax she is more likely than ever to be non-orgasmic.

In sex, as in all other areas of life, we can try too hard to achieve our goals. The tennis player who is desperate to score an ace point frequently serves a double fault. The impoverished actor, desperate for employment, fluffs his lines at his first audition. This phenomenon, known to the layman as Sod's Law, was more properly called the Law of Reversed Effort by its discoverer, Dr Charles Baudoin, the French hypnotherapist.[5]

It occurs because we consciously aim to do one thing, but secretly believe that we will end up doing the opposite. When conflicts such as this arise, our performance generally follows the dictates of our unconscious mind. We are led by our anxieties and fears rather than by our conscious desires. This was recognised by Emil Coué, the founder of autosuggestion, who wrote: 'When the will and the imagination are antagonistic, it is always the imagination which wins.'[6]

This book offers a programme of sexual rejuvenation which needs to be followed in a relaxed and patient fashion. Results *will* come, particularly if you are not struggling too hard for end results. Miracles happen, but not usually overnight, and rarely by the simple wave of a therapeutic wand.

No Can Do

When people expose their bodies, they also lay bare their souls. For this reason I have been privileged, as an osteopath, to have been the confidant of thousands of people who have told me their disappointments, fears, secret longings and sexual frustrations. These are intimate concerns, which perhaps my patients have never discussed before and have been anxious to conceal from their families and friends. Whatever *your* personal difficulties and desires, you can be sure that they are shared by thousands of other people. Everyone wants to retain their youthful vitality and sexual enthusiasm. The recognition of this universal yearning has driven me to write this book.

Some of my patients have been so desperate to regain their sexual vigour that they have become the dupes of quasi-medical rejuvenation clinics. Others have experimented with useless love potions and aphrodisiacs, hoping that to enhance their virility by swallowing a few dozen oysters or by dosing themselves with Royal Bee Jelly – a product which has rightly been dismissed as 'b***** nonsense'. The demand for erotic revival is vast. Dr Stephen Levine, of the University Hospital of

Cleveland, discovered this when he announced that he was seeking volunteers with 'low sexual desire' to test out a new drug which *might* have aphrodisiac properties. The day the invitation was made the hospital telephones were jammed. Over a thousand people offered to test the substance – code-named LY 16530 – which they hoped would help them regain their sexual *joie de vivre*. Weeks later the requests were still pouring in, with the hospital telephonists logging several hundred calls each day.

This is a demand which can and must be met. For over thirty years I have built up a reference library, stocked with medical books and annotated files containing research papers, newspaper cuttings and articles from scientific publications. This vast database is filled with evidence that erotopenia – today's great scourge – *can* be conquered. This book contains the distillation of that accumulated knowledge. (References are supplied where appropriate, both as an acknowledgement of the contribution of this great army of research workers and also to make it possible for you to study their work in greater depth.) The material is offered in a way which I hope you will find informative, entertaining and highly practical.

Loving should be fun, rather than a subject for dry, scientific analysis. This is why I have adopted a lighthearted approach throughout the book, which some may consider inappropriate for so serious a subject. I make no apologies for this apparent frivolity, which is introduced with serious intent, as will become clear later in the book. Sex should also be lyrical, closer to a spontaneous love song than to an ergonomist's time and motion study. This is why I have chosen to use song titles for the book's chapter headings.

As it happens the choice of these titles has provided endless entertainment for my family and friends, and has led to the development of a new party game: the competition to find the most apt theme tunes for people suffering from specific ailments. For instance, the theme tune for flashers might be 'Button up your overcoat' or 'Zip-up-your-doo-dah'. All other examples I'll leave you to discover for yourself! (If you send me your gems on a postcard, I'll do my best to get the collection published.)

This book provides a complete programme of sexual revitalisation offering a wealth of practical advice on subjects ranging from aphrodisiacs and energy diets to pelvic exercises, breath control, Eastern love potions and natural ways of stimulating the output of sex hormones. Each chapter contains a number of tips as well as one or more specific 'Sexercises' for you to practise. These are offered purely as suggested options, for you to make use of as and when you please.

You, and You Alone

Scientists delight in generating statistical averages. These norms are valuable when dealing with subjects *en masse*, but totally useless when trying to predict the performance of an individual at any given time or place. We can talk in general terms about the climate in Brunei – average rainfall, mean humidity and normal range of diurnal temperature – but from these figures it is impossible to predict what the weather will be like on the summit of Kinabalu at five o'clock on the first day of June. So it is with human sexual behaviour, which varies between such extremely wide parameters that there is no such thing as 'normal' sex.

Marie Stopes was one of the great pioneers of sex education. In her best-selling book *Enduring Passion* she related the case histories of two men of roughly comparable age. One had sex three times a day, the other once every two years. Both were healthy and seemingly content with their lot. A statistician, using this small and heavily skewed sample, would deduce that the average frequency of male copulation was 10.5 times a week; a rate which would have frustrated the first of Marie's friends and thoroughly exhausted the second.[7]

The only meaningful yardstick of optimum sexual behaviour is what gives *you* and your partner the maximum contentment and satisfaction. Later in the book we will consider the very real problem of what happens when a three-times-a-day man finds himself living with a twice-a-year partner – an exceedingly common problem which is generally referred to as 'desire incongruity'.

True permissiveness doesn't rest on encouraging everyone to copulate as frequently as possible, with as many partners as possible, in as many positions as possible. True permissiveness depends on giving everyone the freedom to be themselves. This is the object of this book, which sets no targets and recognises no norms. Its object is to help *you* express *your* sexuality in your own, distinctive way.

The book does no more than provide the building bricks by which you can engineer your personal brand of sexual renewal. The choice of the building materials is yours. You are both the architect and builder of your life, which should be as unique and individual as the pattern of loops and whirls on your fingerprints.

Teach Me Tonight

People who really know how to love are as rare as those who really know how to think. Sex is a basic instinct; love is an acquired skill. This

7

is true of all primate animals, for as Californian biologist Dr Robert de Ropp points out: 'Apes, monkeys and men appear to need education in the art of love.'[8] This is demonstrated whenever monkeys are raised in isolation and cannot observe adult courtship and mating behaviour. When they grow up, these untutored infants show 'an almost complete absence of sexual know-how', reports de Ropp.

Human sex has long since ceased to be a mere spasm in the loins, the genital equivalent of an involuntary sneeze. Our cerebral cortex has developed to such an extent that we can now exercise almost total control over our primordial drives. Depending on how we exercise this mastery, sex can be an experience of transcendental beauty and joy, or a mechanical procedure offering little physical pleasure and even less psychological delight. Anything we can learn to do superbly well, we can also learn to do supremely badly. We can learn the delights of gourmet eating, or we can acquire the habits of imprudent feeding. The first makes us happy, the second can give rise to malnutrition and self-inflicted illnesses such as obesity, anorexia and bulimia. With sex we often learn from our mistakes, which means that most of us get a first-class education. But is there not a simpler way to enhance our loving?

We are the masters of our destiny and the captains of our fate. If there is any part of your life you do not welcome or enjoy, change it. And what better time to start than *now*? A bookshop ordered a copy of *How to Revive Your Sex Life* for one of its regular patrons. Two days later they returned the book to the wholesalers with a note: 'Customer couldn't wait.' Such impatience is admirable. Life is far too precious to be wasted. I find it tragic when elderly people review their past lives as an endless succession of unused talents and wasted opportunities. This was the fate of poet Sir John Betjeman who, when asked towards the end of his life if he had any outstanding regrets, replied: 'Not enough sex.'

This book does not set out to offer cures for specific sexual problems. It is not a self-help manual for sufferers from vaginismus or foot and shoe fetishism. If you have such problems seek the help of your doctor or an experienced sex therapist. This is a book which takes a positive approach to sexuality and offers advice to help you increase your sexual vitality and enhance your capacity for love and erotic fulfilment.

For every person suffering from a recognised sexual disease there are probably several dozen who, although not diagnosable 'sick', are nevertheless very conscious of the fact that their love lives are substandard. 'Something is missing,' is the way I often hear it described. 'The excitement has gone out of our sex life.' 'Love-making has lost its sparkle.' 'I go through the motions but sometimes hardly think it's worth the effort.'

It is for this vast audience that this book has been written. If you follow the self-help programme you'll find you'll gain not only sexual drive, but also increased stamina, enthusiasm, vitality, youthfulness and charm. You'll find that in this instance the whole will be far more than the sum of the individual parts. Sexual energy is one of the major driving forces of life, or as ancient Indian sages put it: 'Desire is the root of the universe.'

Sex is 'wholesome' in the true and full meaning of the word. Far from being selfish, it has the power to bring care, and therefore healing, to others. (The word cure derives from the Latin *cura*, meaning care.) Many doctors are now acknowledging this healing force. For instance, Dr Oliver Sacks, discoverer of the first effective remedy for sleeping sickness, who wrote: 'The work of healing, of rendering whole, is first and foremost the business of love.'[9] This is a curative force we should cultivate and extol. 'Long live love!' was the title of a hit song by Chris Andrews. This is the theme and celebratory leitmotiv of this book.

When Love Grows Cold

In the West we think of sex as an inwardly burning fire. Using this metaphor we talk about kindling the flames of love, being consumed with passion, love growing cold and the fires of love being extinguished making people frigid. In the East they have a totally different concept. They visualise love as a sleeping serpent – the living symbol of the goddess Kundalini – which lies dormant in the body waiting to be roused. In using these metaphors both cultures recognise that the energising force of sexual love lies within us all, whatever our age or physical condition. If it is quiescent in some of us at present this is not because it has died or gone away. It is still there, lying dormant, waiting to be aroused.

Each of the chapters which follow is designed to light this inward fire.

SUMMARY
- Lack of sex drive is one of the commonest sexual disorders today – not because it is *untreatable*, but because it is so often allowed to go *untreated*.
- You can increase your sexual vitality, if this is your earnest desire, by following the programme of twenty-three sexercises contained in this book, which are simple, natural and highly effective.

- Don't let your love-making be ruled by the sex manuals. Spontaneity and abandonment are two of the great secrets of sexual fulfilment.
- Don't try too hard to achieve success in bed or you'll evoke the Law of Reversed Effort. You'll set up a conflict between your conscious desire to succeed and your subconscious fear of failure, a battle which will invariably be won by your secret anxieties and fears.
- Put the fun back into your loving and you'll bring the sex back into your life.
- Don't waste time reading statistics about other people's sexual performance. Sexual behaviour is open to such widespread individual variation that it is meaningless to talk in terms of healthy norms. Adopt instead a truly permissive attitude, which means giving yourself the freedom and right to be yourself and do whatever gives *you* sexual pleasure.
- Remember, you are the master of your destiny. If there is anything about your current love life which gives you displeasure, take steps *now* to bring about its change.

Two

The Power of Love

To an impartial observer, our culture must seem to be obsessed with sex. Nipples and bare bottoms swell the circulation of our popular newspapers; explicit, copulatory scenes add spice to the bland pap of television dramas. Sex sells clothes, draws cinema audiences, fuels neighbourhood gossip and fills the pages of blockbuster novels.

Sex is rarely far from our thoughts. Professor Paul Cameron of the University of Louisville, Kentucky discovered this when he interviewed over 4,000 people ranging in age from 8 to 99 and found that the average teenage male had sexual thoughts every minute of his waking day. Even in middle age, when their thoughts might be expected to be preoccupied with other concerns, men turn back to the perennial topic about once every five minutes. (The women in the Kentucky sample had sexual thoughts every two and a half minutes as teenagers and once every ten minutes in middle age.[1])

We are highly erotic animals – 'the most sexually active animal ever', according to Dr Dennis Lincoln, of the Medical Research Council's Reproductive Biology Unit. The prize for sexual vitality doesn't go to the goat, which on a good day can mount 190 ewes and achieve 50 ejaculations. We are the prime sexual athletes because, unlike goats, gorillas and rabbits, we are potentially always 'on heat'. As a result we are, according to Dr Lincoln's calculations, some 10,000 times more sexually prolific than a rabbit.

Doing What Comes Naturally

If we have these lusty proclivities, why do so many people lack sexual vitality and desire? One reason lies embedded in our skulls. The rabbit copulates whenever its hormonal glands decide; we do so only as and when our brains dictate.

We are blessed with a remarkably powerful libidinous drive, and cursed by a super ego which exercises an equally powerful repressive force. We are in fact the only animal which deliberately inhibits its sexual drive, sometimes to the point of making a virtue of total celibacy.

11

It is as if we were cavalry soldiers entering the fray on a powerful percheron charger which we choose to restrain by hobbling its feet and reining it back on a powerful snaffle bit.

We have within ourselves the potential for ecstasy or despair. This is the primordial, animal force which empowers our lives. Freud thought of it as the dark unconscious force of the id; Plato as the daemon within. Philosophers have always sought to distinguish between the forces of reason and the forces of passion. They have visualised a constant battle between the head and the heart; an eternal struggle between the rival powers of Apollo and Dionysus. Theologians have gone even further, and have identified the clash as the perennial conflict between the forces of good and evil. These are false dichotomies. Passion is a God-given gift, just as much as our more recently acquired faculties of intellect and reason.

The daemon or genius within is our source of vitality, enthusiasm and creative fire. A man is a genius not because he is a great writer or painter; he is a great writer or painter because he is possessed by genius. This was recognised by Goethe, who argued that the daemonic force of man was the fountainhead of culture, poetry, music, religion and patriotic fervour. People who have this dynamic energy are not necessarily highly intelligent, he wrote, 'yet a tremendous force emanates from them, they possess an incredible force over all other creatures and even over the elements; nobody can say how far their influence will reach'. This is the primeval force which Bergson called *élan vital*, and Freud libido.

Our task is simply to harness and utilise this feral force.

Something Wonderful

Sex is one of the most powerful of all human instincts. In the cause of love we perpetrate the most horrendous *crimes passionels*, commit suicide, waste away, abandon our children or renounce a throne. Love is the power which conquers all, moves mountains, leaps barriers and laughs at locksmiths. This is a force which needs to be cultivated rather than tamed.

Somewhere along the line many of us have learned to subdue this drive and quench this passion. We have fostered a culture in which it is fashionable to curb our enthusiasm and conceal our emotions. Children are taught to 'play it cool'; adults to maintain a stiff upper lip. We have erected a shield to protect us from the depths of emotional pain, which now bars us from experiencing the heights of emotional pleasure. We suffer sexual apathy, not because we are sick, but because we have chosen to become *a-pathos* – without feeling.

To escape this malaise we must lower our emotional defences and open ourselves once more to the experience of passion. We must rekindle our zest for life. This will bring us joy as well as sexual vitality, for as Bertrand Russell observed, 'zest is the secret of happiness and well-being'.

Few children today are taught the old Greek legends. If they were, they might learn a vital lesson in loving from the story of Aphrodite's visit to the oracle Themis. Aphrodite was concerned that Eros, her son, was failing to mature. She lavished care on him, and yet the young love god remained a small, chubby, rosy-cheeked child. When she consulted Themis, the prophetess quickly diagnosed the cause. 'Love cannot grow without passion,' she warned. Our trouble today is that we try to divorce sex from love, and love from passion.

Love is a Many-Splendoured Thing

Several factors hold us back from developing an uninhibited lust for life. The first is a misguided attempt to separate our affectional lives into watertight compartments.

The Greeks divided love into three categories: *eros* (sexual love), *agape* (altruistic love) and *philia* (brotherly love). Others have carried the fragmentation further still, like psychoanalyst Eric Fromm, who divides love into five basic categories: brotherly love, maternal love, erotic love, self love and love of God.[2]

All such divisions are purely arbitrary. These classifications are harmless in themselves, but troubles arise when they are hijacked by pietists and used to create moral hierarchies. At the top they place the 'noble' expressions of love – adoration, altruism and maternal love. At the bottom the 'debased' forms – narcissism and sexual lust. This ranking is false and artificially divisive. Love may have many faces, but they are all expressions of the same human need for warm, intimate, interpersonal relationships. Freud recognised this in his later years and broadened his concept of libido until it took on a meaning closer to generalised life energy. This is equally true of Jung, who held that there is one single life force which fuels all types of human activity – sexual, social, cultural and creative.

Love cannot be confined in watertight compartments. Should we admire the woman who shows her maternal love by nursing her child through a fretful night, but condemn her if she confesses that she gets sensual pleasure from suckling the infant to her breast? In the same way, can we say that sexual relations between men and women are always purely carnal? As a correspondent to *Forum* magazine recognised: 'Sex is in little private jokes and secret smiles across the table at breakfast . . . Sex is preparing a special meal together and exchanging innermost thoughts over a bottle of wine, in the gentlest kiss at the back of the neck and holding hands watching television.'[3]

The sex researchers have done us a great disservice by fostering the idea that sexual love is confined to a brief, mechanical coupling which begins in coitus and ends in orgasm. This telescopes a wide-ranging human passion into an ephemeral, calisthenic rite.

Some of the blame for this impoverishment must be laid at the door of Alfred Kinsey, who turned sex into a subject, not of passion, but of cold, statistical research. Born in New Jersey, of pious Victorian parents, Kinsey showed little interest in sex as a teenager. At school dances he played the piano while his class-mates took the floor and gave vertical expression to their horizontal desires.

His first scientific paper, 'What Do Birds Do When It Rains?', was based on many hours of outdoor observation. Years later, still the voyeur, he made a similarly detailed study of 18,000 American males. Being a scientist, he urgently needed to generate statistics. Since he couldn't measure the extent of human love, or the strength of sexual desire, he invented a numerate yardstick of human sexuality called the 'total outlet'. This referred to the total number of orgasms a person had per week, whether from intercourse, masturbation, wet dreams, petting or bestiality.

The data was eventually published as the Kinsey Report, a massive study which revealed a vast amount about patterns of human copulation, but nothing at all about the romance or passion of love. The subject which had inspired generations of poets and painters was now consigned to the laboratory, where it has become, like a cadaver on a pathologist's bench, the subject of dispassionate scientific scrutiny. This has encouraged us to treat sex as a mechanical, genitally focused act, rather than an all-embracing life force.

New Kind of Love

Freud, like Kinsey, played his own part in quenching the Dionysian fires. He was a pioneer who, with very little data to work with, developed several remarkably accurate concepts. Unfortunately he also generated several dangerous myths, one of which was his concept of the 'sublimation' of sexual energy. Freud believed that the supply of libido was as fixed as the fuel in a butane lighter.

According to this teaching, if sex energy is expended on one or other of Kinsey's 'total outlets', there is that much less for other purposes. We can't expend our passions in bed and still have energy left for higher purposes – acts of philanthropy or works of scientific creativity. The driving force behind all great works of art, Freud claimed, arose from the 'sublimation' of libido. We are inspired to write poetry, or impelled to show an affection for stray cats, because our sexual energies are diverted to these purposes.

But love is not an expendable resource which needs to be conserved like a fossil fuel. Love is a fire which grows the more fiercely it burns. As ye sow, so shall ye reap. Give love, and you will get love.

Freud's sublimation theory is still widely held, and yet there is no evidence that sexual abstinence is an aid to creativity. The sexually repressed have undoubtedly produced some splendid poetry, music and literature, but then so too have sexual libertines like Stendhal, Goethe, Byron, Balzac, Boswell and Burns. Karl Marx made a major contribution to twentieth-century thought, but hardly by sublimating his sex drive. He had a Promethean capacity for sex, according to his biographers, and as well as maintaining a loving relationship with his wife also found time for numerous extra-marital affairs. Not only did he seduce the family maid, by whom he had an illegitimate son, he also maintained a tumultuous affair with a cousin twenty years his junior.

Albert Einstein, another of the century's most innovative personalities, also managed to satisfy his keen sexual appetite while pursuing his studies and developing the Theory of Relativity. During this time, according to his housekeeper, he had several mistresses, one of whom was an attractive Austrian blonde, many years younger than his wife, whom he took on regular sailing trips.

As the lives of Marx and Einstein demonstrate, sexual passion and creativity are complementary rather than antagonistic. If you develop a lust for life, you generate the energy for sex and also the enthusiasm for work and the zest for play. People with sexual vitality are successful, not only in bed, but also in other spheres of their life. They are happier and relaxed. They suffer fewer tension ailments – chronic fatigue, insomnia, fibrositis, indigestion and tension headaches – for, as psychoanalyst Wilhelm Reich observed, 'the setting free of genital energies has great therapeutic effect'.[4] They are also more likely to succeed in business, according to Dr David Reuben, who claims: 'The more potent a man is in the bedroom, the more potent he is in business.'

The search for sexual vitality is therefore far more than a mere quest for carnal satisfaction. It is an essential expression of the basic human desire to live life to the full, and to grow rather than stagnate.

Don't Fence Me In

Freud believed that civilisation could be achieved only if we kept firm control of our animal passions. There must be conscious restraints, he felt, or life would become an endless promiscuous orgy. If a housewife wants to live at peace with her neighbour, she cannot seduce the woman's husband every time the urge takes her. That much is clear. But it can also be argued that love is the strongest of all civilising forces. In Tantric yoga, sex is used as a means of achieving cosmic union. A similar belief was held by the ancient Chinese, who claimed: 'Sexual intercourse is the human counterpart of the cosmic process.' One medieval school of Jewish kabbalists went one stage further and claimed that *all* creation was upheld by sexual activity. So strong was this belief that they predicted that if sexual activity ceased, the earth would disintegrate like a snowman melting in the sun.

The concept of sex as a holy sacrament is foreign to our current way of thinking. Yet in truth, sex is neither sacred nor profane. It is like atomic energy, a power for good or a power for ill. It all depends on the way the force is used.

Freedom is not licence. We need to control our animal instincts otherwise we become the slaves of passion. This is the fate the Puritans feared and the Stoics struggled to avoid. But the choice is not between unbridled licence and total celibacy. Passion without self-control is licence; passion with control is liberation. The ancient Indian sages visualised man as a horse-drawn chariot, the horses representing the animal passions which impelled him forward, and the charioteer the guiding hand of intellect and reason. The horses were needed to provide the power, the driver to provide the direction.

We are often too frightened to release the power of the daemon within. We are afraid to cry, in case we lose control. We shrink back from losing our temper, for fear that we will be unable to control the forces we unleash. Occasionally we are reluctant to submit to a general anaesthetic, in case we expose the Rabelaisian side of our characters which we are normally so careful to conceal. In the same way we are sometimes reluctant to fall in love, in case we fall victim to the disease which the Age of Chivalry dubbed 'love sickness', or 'the divine madness'.

16

In suppressing passion man has escaped being a beast only to become a robot. We must help the next generation to avoid this trap. Our aim should be to bring up children who, in the words of Thomas Henry Huxley, are 'full of life and fire, but whose passions are trained to come to heel by a vigorous will'.[5]

Sexual passion is an excellent servant, but a tyrannical master. Far from suppressing our amorous desires, we should give them every encouragement we can. Every day should be a celebration of the power of human love. The more we extol this virtue, the stronger it will grow.

Sexercise 1
The Aphrodisiac Album

If you are hungry you can stimulate the flow of digestive juices by looking at a picture of a succulent plate of Steak Diane, or by reading a gourmet's account of a cordon bleu meal. So it is with sexual desire. If you want to stimulate your loving urge, focus your attention on anything which inspires your love.

Buy a large album, give it a suitable title like 'Loving Mementos', and fill it with everything which stimulates loving thoughts. Incorporate pages from treasured love letters, romantic holiday snapshots, snatches of erotic poetry and the lyrics of songs that are of special romantic significance. When the album is full, festoon your bedroom with the overflow of amorous memorabilia, surrounding yourself with permanent reminders of those delightful times when you were head-over-heels in love.

Dr Helen Kaplan, one of the world's leading authorities on the treatment of reduced libido, considers that romantic nostalgia has rejuvenating powers. As she explains: 'The connections of the sex centres to the parts of the brain that process and store experience make sexual desire highly sensitive to the past.'[6]

Every time you delve into your romantic album, you will stimulate these association pathways, and experience a warm, amorous glow.

SUMMARY
- Sexual drive is a potent force within us all, whatever our age or physical condition. One simple way to release its power is to lift the floodgates – the deep-seated inhibitions and cultural taboos – which check its flow.

- 'Love cannot grow without passion' the Greek oracle proclaimed. Become a more passionate, sensuous person and you will automatically kindle the flames of desire. We suffer sexual apathy, not because we are sick, but because we have chosen to become *a-pathos*, without feeling.
- Give love freely – not only to your bed-mate, but also to your neighbours, family and friends – and you will gain love. For love is not an expendable resource; it is a fire which grows the more fiercely it burns.
- To stimulate that loving feeling, make a conscious practice of focusing your attention on things which you know will inspire your love, like pictures of your honeymoon, old love letters and erotic poetry. Build these into an aphrodisiac album, which you can turn to whenever you want to feel amorous, and you will find that 'sexual desire is highly sensitive to the past', as sexologist Dr Helen Kaplan observed.

Three

Two Sleepy People

Chronic fatigue is one of the major disorders of our age. Persistent tiredness impairs our efficiency at work, renders us prone to accidents, makes us irritable with our family and friends – and plays havoc with our love lives.

'I believe fatigue to be the greatest enemy a woman ever faces,' claimed Dr Marion Hilliard, head of Obstetrics and Gynaecology at the Woman's College Hospital, Toronto. 'It robs her of the joy and vitality without which any life is grey and meaningless.' When asked, towards the end of her career, what was the commonest cause of sexual distress, she had no hesitation in replying: 'The first and most important thing is fatigue. No doubt about it, a happy married life takes energy!'[1]

When you're exhausted the bedroom becomes a place for sleep, not an arena for sexual fun and games. On honeymoon all you want to do is sleep and make love. Ten years later you still want to sleep and make love – but now it's at the same time! This book offers numerous techniques for improving bodily vim and vigour. These will improve your lust for life as well as your zest for loving.

Body and Soul

Health is a unity, and for this reason it is impossible to write an honest book about sexual rejuvenation which doesn't at the same time become a guide to general well-being. Many of the factors which give rise to reduced libido – tension, tiredness, anxiety and an inadequate diet – also predispose to other illnesses. This was recognised many years ago by the British government in an early handbook, *Health Education*. 'It is almost impossible to avoid working from the part towards the whole,' the report concluded, 'so that what began as a consideration of health ends up as a study of the good life.'[2] This book adopts a holistic approach and embraces the hope that what begins as a programme of sexual regeneration will also serve as a blueprint for 'the good life'.

If we lack physical fitness we cannot expect to enjoy a full, exciting sex life. Equally, one must agree with Dr Paul Pearson, Director of

Education at the Kinsey Institute, that 'there can be no health without sexual health'.[3]

The great deficiency of modern sexology is that it tries to treat one small aspect of human behaviour in isolation from the rest. We are not just a collection of physical organs – penis, clitoris, vagina and breasts. We also have higher centres in our brain, where we express our feelings, dreams and spiritual aspirations. This was the main weakness of the Kinsey Report, according to New York psychiatrist Dr Sol Ginsburg; that it took sex out of context, 'as though it existed without any relationship to goals, values, ambitions, hopes and desires'.[4]

To achieve fulfilment – in whatever field – we must avoid this artificial schism between body and mind, and create a wholesome fusion of all aspects of our personality.

There'll Never Be Another You

In essence the study of human personality is the investigation of individual difference. People show a consistent variation in the way they behave. Some are by nature confident and cheerful; others timid and morose. These personality dispositions are deeply etched into our psyches. This is why the Greeks spoke about a person's 'character', a word which originally meant 'engraving'.

Any theory of human sexuality must acknowledge the wide range of sexual behaviour. Some of us are inherently lustier than others. (The *Kama Sutra* divides people into three categories according to their normal level of sexual desire – Small, Middling and Intense.[5]) This is why it is foolish to judge yourself against the statistical norms. If you're by nature a once-a-fortnight person, nothing on earth is going to convert you into a twice-a-day-and-three-times-on-Sundays sexual athlete. If you're turned on by butterflies rather than bare bottoms, stick to lepidopterology. Do what comes naturally – and enjoy it!

Over the years there have been numerous attempts to divide people into clear-cut types. All these typographies have acknowledged that some folk are sexier than others. This variance has often been linked with differences in body build.

In the second century the Hindus believed that men could be divided into *satviks*, *rajasiks* or *tamasiks*. The first were of medium height and build and were pure-minded and wise; the second tall, muscular, energetic and passionate; and the third lay in between.[6] A somewhat similar theory was introduced in the middle of the present century by Dr William Sheldon, who divided people according to their body build into ectomorphs, endomorphs and mesomorphs. The first are slender, small-boned and introverted; the second chubby, emotional and extroverted; and the third muscular, athletic and self-assertive.[7]

It is often claimed that obese women overeat to make themselves unattractive to the opposite sex. This roly-poly defence mechanism may occasionally be used, but the general burden of evidence suggests that fat women tend to be sexier than their slim counterparts. They have a lust for life which expresses itself in a passion for food and an equal craving for sex.

This was suggested by a study of married women carried out at the Michael Reese Hospital in Chicago. It compared the sex lives of matched groups of fat and slim women. The results showed that 'in terms of erotic readiness and general sexual excitability' the fat women were nearly twice as sensuous as the slim. 'These women obviously weren't overeating *instead* of having sex;' the researchers concluded, 'their craving for both food and sex exists almost simultaneously.'[8]

This may explain why men generally show a penchant for voluptuous women, because they expect them to be more willing and exciting lovers. Ours is an unusual culture in this respect, for we seem to prefer the anorexic, model-girl figure to the Venus with the generous curves of a Botticelli nude. Historically this is rare. A global study of twenty-six tribes revealed that all but five liked their women fat. The Sirione, natives of the Amazon River basin, were fairly typical in this respect. According to an anthropologist's report, the Sirione men had a very clear picture of their ideal female partner. 'Besides being young, a desirable sex partner should also be fat. She should have big hips, good-sized but firm breasts, and a deposit of fat on her sexual organs.'[9] This, not surprisingly, makes her sound like the fertility goddesses represented in prehistoric sculptures.

Extroverts are another group who appear to have a special appetite for sex. A German study of a group of over 6,000 male and female students indicated that people with outward-looking personalities show greater eroticism than those who are inclined to be more introspective. The extrovert girls, for example, had intercourse more than twice as often as their introvert class-mates. They also began petting earlier, were younger when they had their first coital experience and were sexually more adventurous in later life, being more likely to experiment with different coital positions and to adopt techniques like fellatio and cunnilingus. They also tended to be more promiscuous and were more than twice as likely to report that they were 'nearly always' orgasmic when they had sex.[10]

Since we can't alter our genetic make-up, we are unable to transform

21

ourselves into chubby extroverts, even if we wished. But no doubt we could all benefit by being a trifle less introspective.

They Can't Take That Away From Me

Sex has its psychology and physiology – and also its mythology. Many people still believe that their health will suffer if they abandon themselves to the pleasures of the flesh.

Victorian youngsters were warned that if they masturbated they would suffer lassitude, physical weakness, loss of memory, fits, mental degeneration and progressively failing eyesight. Hearing this, one youngster asked: 'If wanking makes you blind, couldn't I just do it until I'm short-sighted?' Even adult men were cautioned to preserve their health and strength by limiting their sexual activity. 'One drop of semen is worth sixty drops of blood', they were warned. This idea was first promoted in the *Tao of Love-making*, which suggested that men should preserve their energies and vital fluids by ejaculating only once in every hundred coitions. Judging by the subsequent growth of the Chinese population, this must have been a maxim 'more honour'd in the breach than the observance'.

The belief that sex is weakening still persists in sporting circles. Boxers are advised to conserve their strength by observing a period of celibacy before a big fight. (Not all observe this bar, for example, John Conteh who, when asked if sex before a fight affected his performance, replied: 'Which performance?')

Some sports trainers insist that athletes observe a similar curfew. This is a totally pointless restriction, as Professor Manfred Steinback discovered when he investigated the sex lives of 800 athletes taking part in the Munich Olympic Games. 'Coaches who think they can improve their protégés' sporting achievements by banishing them from the boudoir are wasting their time,' he reported. 'If an athlete does feel substandard after a night on the tiles it is not sex that has sapped his strength but the attendant frivolities such as drinking, dancing and dashing around until the early hours of the morning.'[11]

The effect of sex on athletic performance is likely to be beneficial rather than detrimental, according to evidence presented to doctors attending a recent sports medicine conference in Vienna. Women could improve their chances of winning a medal, they were told, if they had a 'turbulent, amorous event' before they ran.[12]

This is not surprising, for sex is an excellent way of overcoming pre-performance anxiety and tensions. Certainly there is no evidence

22

whatsoever that sex is harmful, even when indulged in to a prodigious extent. Kinsey reported the case of a man who remained hale and hearty despite having had intercourse thirty times a week for thirty years. He also reported a similar instance of a woman who suffered no ill effects from having an average of seventy orgasms a week.

One wonders how masturbation got its debilitating reputation. In Egypt the practice is popularly referred to as 'Thirty-nine', because for some reason it is believed that masturbation is thirty-nine times more exhausting than normal copulation. If this were true our schools and workplaces would be either empty, or full of walking zombies, since 99 per cent of males and 82 per cent of females masturbate, according to the surveys carried out by Shere Hite.

So Tired

What, then, is the source of the ubiquitous belief that sex is weakening? As this is largely a masculine fear, is it possible that men throughout the ages have misinterpreted their post-orgasmic drowsiness? Have they made the mistake of attributing their lassitude to a sudden depletion of bodily energy, rather than to a rapid, and wholly beneficial, reduction in bodily tension?

Patients have often told me that they find sex the finest cure for tension when they are under stress. This, certainly, was true for President Kennedy. At a conference of heads of state in Nassau, he confided to Britain's Prime Minister, Harold Macmillan, that if he went too long without a woman he developed tension headaches. Apparently there was no shortage of women willing to act as his relaxation therapists, including Marilyn Monroe, who returned from a rendezvous with J.F.K. and told a friend: 'I think I made his back feel better.'

The Greeks had few qualms about sex, which they considered wholly therapeutic. Aristotle was convinced that coition lightened the body and dissipated mental ills. Many doctors since then have recommended it as a cure for conditions ranging from the 'green sickness' to lassitude, lumbago, eye strain, pre-menstrual tension and period pain. Erasmus, Charles Darwin's unconventional doctor brother, advocated it as a cure for hypochondriasis.[13] Wilhelm Reich believed that an uninhibited sex life enhanced a person's higher mental faculties. His argument, which doesn't seem wholly unreasonable, was that 'in order to repress his sexual tendencies and desires the individual must use up a large amount of physical energy. This inhibits and injures the development of other activities'.[14]

23

It's No Sin

Many people dampen their sexual drive because they harbour the ancient fear that sex is harmful. Others hold their erotic desire in check because they believe that sex is 'dirty'. This is a product of modern moral teaching, which would have been totally alien to our pagan forebears. They *worshipped* the gods of fertility and sex, which often took the form of bulls or rams or other animals of conspicuous sexual energy. Shiva, one of the principal gods in the Hindu pantheon, is regarded as the universal source of energy. His symbol is the *linga*, which is fashioned in the unmistakable shape of an erect penis. Similar sex symbols featured prominently in European religious festivals. Temples became the sites of sexual rites and group orgies, where prostitutes served their gods by indulging in 'sacrificial sex'.

This may seem strange to us today, and distinctly sacrilegious. Yet sex is as much a part of God's creation as the air we breathe. If we can worship the Almighty in acts of devotion and charity, why not in acts of love? This may be one way of overcoming our sexual inhibitions, according to Professor Goldberg, a leading authority on the role of sex in religious ritual and behaviour. 'It was in the temple that man made an art of his loving, an *ars amandi*,' he wrote, 'which Western man has well nigh forgotten. And not until he relearns this sacred art will he be completely happy again.'[15]

Sexual love bridges the gap between the sacred and the profane, the sublime and the banal, the holy and the downright Rabelaisian. In the merging of two bodies we express the union of the yang and yin, the universal male and female principles. For a few moments in the act of sexual congress we lose our individual identities and achieve a measure of cosmic union. In sex we find freedom, joy and transcendental expression.

This oceanic feeling was well expressed by Bertrand Russell, who wrote: 'I have sought love, first because it brings ecstasy – ecstasy so great that I would have sacrificed all the rest of life for a few hours of this joy. I have sought it next because it relieves loneliness – that terrible loneliness in which one's shivering consciousness looks over the world into the cold, unfathomable, lifeless abyss. I have sought it, finally, because in the union of love I have seen, in a mystic miniature, the pre-figuring vision of the heaven that saints and poets have imagined.'

Many years ago, Hippocrates propounded the Law of Use, which states: 'That which is used develops; that which is not used wastes away.' This is as true of sexual potency as it is of the muscles of the arms

24

and legs. If we use our sexual powers, they are strengthened; if we neglect them they will waste away.

These concepts take us a long way from the Victorian image of sex as a degrading, bestial act, which was tolerated in certain carefully circumscribed circumstances only because it was essential for the perpetuation of the human race.

'Many world religions have accepted the divine origin of the sex urge and have encouraged their followers to praise God for their sexuality. They recognised that sexual energy was an integral part of the life force and advised people to call on the Almighty for an increase of libido.'

This suggestion may seem bizarre, even impious, but it has an old, and thoroughly respectable, pedigree. Omar Haleeby, sexual adviser to the prophet Mohammed, suggested that couples should say a brief prayer before embarking on the act of sexual congress. This idea is not as strange as it may at first seem, for if one can say grace before meals, and a prayer before going to sleep, why not a petition before making love?

The Zoroastrians, like the Muslims, observed this practice, believing that the act of coitus was consummated in the presence of God, who caused it to be rewarded by the blessings of emotional fulfilment and transcendental bliss. So why not a lover's prayer – of supplication and thanksgiving – to be said last thing at night and immediately before having intercourse?

At present the prayer books of the world's major faiths seem to show little interest in the sex lives of their followers. My personal research revealed only one such recorded petition. Written for the benefit of married couples (naturally), it acknowledges the importance of a healthy sexual relationship and incorporates the plea: 'Please help us not to forget that the sign of our sacrament, the sexual expression of our love, makes you present in our home.' (The author would be delighted to receive notice of any other published prayers which relate to any aspect of human sexuality.)

In the absence of a recognised petition, try reciting the following prayer last thing at night and immediately before making love. 'May the Almighty, who is infinite love and infinite joy, fulfil me/us with erotic energy, imbue me/us with eternal love and bless my life/our lives with joyous and abundant sexuality.'

In addition, why not follow another of Omar Haleeby's recommendations? He advised Muslims to give thanks by shouting the name Allah whenever they reached a climax. If you're not a Muslim, you can pay tribute to your own particular deity. I am told that many Italian men let out an ecstatic 'Madonna Mia!' at the moment of orgasm, but I have no proof of this. Alternatively, you could just shout 'Hallelujah!', a word originally derived from the Hebrew for 'Praise ye the Lord'. It's a nice way of showing your gratitude and celebrating your success – and a pleasant way of letting your partner know you've come!

Words have power to influence the subconscious mind, whether they're religious prayers or secular petitions.

Sexercise 2
The Coué Mantra

Emil Coué demonstrated that the body is strongly influenced by the mind, and more especially by the imagination. If we are suffering from insomnia, we can woo the muse of sleep by implanting into our subconscious mind the thought that our eyelids are drooping and our bodies growing progressively heavier and heavier. If we feel one degree under, we can recapture our lost vitality by reciting as we fall asleep: 'Everyday in every way I'm getting better and better.'

A similar technique can be used to overcome erotopenia – which is a convenient Greek abbreviation for 'lack of sex drive'. The procedure is simple. When we relax and are on the threshold of sleep our subconscious minds are highly amenable to suggestion. At this time say quietly to yourself: 'Every day from now onwards I am going to find my sexual energy increasing and my lust for life growing.' Repeat this every night, and believe fervently in what you are saying, and gradually your sexual vitality will grow.

SUMMARY

- Loss of libido is often a symptom of tiredness, stress and poor physical condition. Get yourself fit – by following a programme of sensible eating, exercise, rest and relaxation – and you'll recover your lust for life and zest for love.
- Although you cannot change your inherited personality structure, there is strong reason to believe that the more extrovert you are in your behaviour – friendly, carefree and jolly – the more lively your sex life will become.
- Muscles waste away if they're not used. Exactly the same happens to sexual function, which observes the Hippocratic Law of Use: 'That which is used develops, that which is not used wastes away.' In Victorian times it was thought that sex was weakening; now it's known that sexual potency grows the more it is exercised. 'Use it or lose it.'

- Sexual libido can be increased by autosuggestion. Every night, when you begin to feel drowsy, fill your subconscious mind with thoughts of growing sexual energy, saying to yourself: 'Every day from now onwards I am going to find my sexual energy increasing and my lust for life growing.'
- Follow the example of Dr Omar Haleeby, and constantly utter a prayer of thanks for the power of love. This will remind you that sex is not degrading or sinful but a God-given gift through which we can achieve a sense of cosmic union and transcendental bliss.

Four

Let Yourself Go

The Romantic poets believed that love was an affliction of the heart, an *affaire de coeur*. How wrong they were. The seat of love is not the heart or even the groin. Sex is primarily a function of the brain.

Thought control alone is enough to give some people an orgasm. A few, highly reactive women can reach a climax simply by entering a world of fantasy, reaching the point of ecstasy by imagining perhaps that they're being stripped and seduced by a wildly attractive stranger. A still more remarkable demonstration of grey-cell sex is currently on show in Russia, where a charismatic faith healer called Boris Zolotov is holding 'sexual healing seminars' attended by thousands of frustrated Russian women. The press have branded him a 'sex maniac' and the local church has accused him of being in league with the devil, because he uses thought force to stimulate his audience and induce an orgasm in as many as thirty women at a time.[1]

Only Make-Believe

The potency of most of the old love potions, spells and charms was derived from autosuggestion. If you think that swallowing a dozen oysters will enable you to outperform Casanova, it almost certainly will. A medieval treatise on witchcraft, called *Necromancy, Witches and Sorcerers*[2], tells the delightful tale of a young man who attended a house party taking with him a 'magic' cake. Any girl who sampled the cake would fall immediately under his spell, he boasted. A young girl, somewhat bolder than the rest, laughingly took up the challenge and munched a large slice of what was actually a perfectly normal piece of confectionery. Intellectually she *knew* she couldn't be so easily seduced, and yet she couldn't totally rid her mind of the seeds of doubt. During the night those small seeds grew and the magic took hold. She couldn't sleep for thinking of the fascinating stranger and his tantalising spell. Eventually, to ease her restlessness, she felt impelled to visit the young man's room. Like Trilby, she was drawn inexorably to her Svengali. She called to demand an explanation, but stayed the night to be comforted in his arms. This eased her tension and also fulfilled his boast.

All I Have To Do is Dream

Sex is far more often a thought than a response to an outside stimulus. This is particularly true at night when, freed of the restraints of our conscious mind, we can give free rein to our erotic imaginings. This is the time when men indulge their fantasies to the full, dreaming of group orgies and bare-breasted maidens tethered to bedposts, powerless to resist their insatiable demands. For men the bedroom is the commonest site of cerebral sex, with four-fifths of men experiencing wet dreams at some time in their lives.[3] (For some men this is the only time they have an orgasm.)

Women also have erotic dreams. This has been demonstrated using a photoplethysmograph, a transparent plastic tube which is inserted into the vagina to measure the engorgement of the vaginal walls. Using this device it has been possible to show that during dream sleep, which occurs approximately every ninety minutes, women show all the typical signs of sexual arousal.[4] It is reckoned that one in three women have orgasms as a result of erotic dreams. We may be sexually abstemious by day, but we rarely are by night!

Puppet on a String

The neural centre responsible for sexual arousal is located in a part of the brain known as the limbic system. This erotic powerhouse is stimulated by thoughts, and also by a wide range of physical sensations – visual, tactile, auditory and olfactory. It responds to a provocative glance, a lightly stroked thigh, a whiff of perfume or a few lines of erotic poetry. 'When this system is active,' explains Dr Helen Kaplan, 'a person is "horny". He may feel genital sensations, or he may feel vaguely sexy, or even just restless.'[5]

Sexual arousal can be enhanced by stimulating the brain's limbic centre in a variety of different ways, which will be discussed at length in later sections of the book. The sex centre acts as a puppet master. When the cerebral strings are pulled, we dance; maybe a lively jig, an erotic tango or a funeral march. It all depends on the way the strings are manipulated. But what if the puppet master goes on strike, and decides he doesn't want us to perform at all?

Sex drive in all animals is a balance between the forces of stimulation and the forces of inhibition. Like a car, the brain is provided with both an accelerator and a brake. As a result, a reduction in libido can be caused by either a lack of excitation or an excess of inhibition. This, unfortunately, is where humans outperform every other living creature. In the course of our evolution we have developed a powerful cerebral cortex which enables us to maintain a stranglehold over our animal passions. It is the excessive use of this control which produces most cases of psychogenic erotopenia.

Please Release Me

Masters and Johnson demonstrated that the human sexual response – tumescence, increased lubrication and orgasm – is under the control of the autonomic nervous system. As such the response is similar to other essential bodily functions, such as heartbeat, digestion and excretion. But there is one vital difference, namely that sex, unlike all the body's other vegetative functions, is highly responsive to cognitive control. We can readily increase or decrease our level of sexual arousal whereas, unless we're highly trained *yogis*, we can't as easily modify our pulse rate or stomach contractions.

This makes it possible to develop a high degree of mastery over the brain's sex centres. By using the techniques outlined in this book you'll find it possible to raise or lower your level of sexual excitation at will. The first step in gaining this mastery is to assume control of the brain's inhibitory centres.

The genital organs themselves know neither guilt nor shame. These are both mental constructs. Babies are not ashamed of their naked bodies, they are not afraid to enjoy sensuous pleasures, and feel no embarrassment whatsoever when they play with their genitalia. These are anxieties which we acquire in the course of our upbringing. These are the 'man-forged manacles' which William Blake described: the sexual taboos, anxieties and fears which curb our freedom of sexual expression.

Climb Every Mountain

Physicists claim that a match contains within its substance enough atomic energy to flatten a mountain. So it is with us. Inside every human body there lies a vast store of untapped sexual energy. The sex therapist's main task is to release this inner power by removing the psychological blocks which limit its flow.

A useful analogy is with the treatment of anorexic patients. Their fundamental problem is psychosomatic. They know *how* to eat, *where* to eat and *when* to eat. Their trouble is that they are programmed *not* to eat. Restore their desire for food and they will be well. But would anyone suggest that they could be helped by being taught how to chew? Why, then, should we expect to aid people with disordered sexual appetites by teaching them how to copulate? It's thought processes which need changing, not coital positions.

This is something the medieval doctors discovered and we seem to have forgotten. For years physicians struggled to decide whether disorders of sexual desire were diseases of the head, heart or sex organs. The matter was finally settled by Peter of Spain, a remarkable man who taught medicine in Siena and eventually progressed to become Pope in 1276. He decided that lack of ardour was primarily a disorder of the brain rather than the testicles.

This is now a well-established medical belief. Experiments show that one of the brain's major centres of sexual inhibition lies at each side of the cerebral hemispheres, in regions known as the temporal lobes. If the activity of these areas is deadened by drink, sexual repressions fly out of the window. If it is inhibited by a general anaesthetic, even prim maiden ladies may lift up their skirts and swear like troopers.

In the past experiments were carried out on animals which would not be tolerated today. They showed that when the temporal lobes of male monkeys were destroyed surgically they became 'sex-obsessed to the point of insanity'. When they were alone, they masturbated indiscriminately, even if they were falling asleep or dangling upside-down from the roof of their cage. If they were in groups, they became insatiable sex maniacs, copulating continually and indiscriminately with males, females, keepers, cage walls and anything else that came to hand.[6]

Similar experiments with tom cats produced equally startling behaviour. Without their sex inhibitory centres the cats indulged in what the researchers described as 'tandem copulation'. Rising to abnormal heights of passion, three or four toms in a row would mount each other, like a line of stacked supermarket trolleys. At other times, to satisfy their unrestrained urges, they would copulate with dogs, monkeys and, on one occasion, even an elderly hen.[7]

Anything Goes

In a cultured society we cannot behave like brain-damaged monkeys or cats. We can't satisfy our passions by mounting the neighbour's bull

31

terrier, or by indulging in tandem copulation in the supermarket check-out queue. These urges must be controlled if we are going to live in orderly communities.

Freud spent his life investigating the ways in which civilised men and women subjugate their animal passions. Many repress them. Some try to sublimate them. A number deny them. Others use a coping technique which Freud called projection. This technique was favoured by a man who visited a psychologist for a personality test. First he was shown a card with a single line drawn on it. 'What do you imagine when you look at this?' he was asked.

'Sex,' he replied.

Then he was shown a card with a circle on it. 'What about this?' Again the picture triggered off sexual images. The next card carried a triangle. 'What does this bring to mind?'

Once again the man had no doubts. 'Sex,' he replied.

At this point the psychologist put down the pack of cards and said: 'In my opinion you have an obsession with sex.'

The young man was staggered. '*I* have an obsession!' he spluttered. 'That's ripe coming from you. You're the one who's producing all the filthy postcards.'

Psychological defence mechanisms like this can be used to control our sexual responses, but they can be overdone. Tests show that sexual satisfaction is negatively correlated with shyness, disgust and prudishness.[8] We can be too coy for our own good. The moral programmes which are fed into our temporal lobes during childhood can be excessively inhibiting. This can make it difficult, or even impossible, for us as adults to enjoy a normal, healthy sex life.

In these cases the lack of sex drive results from an excess of inhibitory control. The power is there waiting to be released, just as the sun is shining even on overcast days when its energy and warmth are obscured by a dense cloud cover. Roll back the clouds, lift the straitjacket of inhibitions, and the power comes flooding through.

Maybe It's Because

Our sexual mores, like our customs, language and diet, are determined by our cultural background. We are born with exactly the same sex drive as a Somalian peasant or Singaporean potentate. We inherit the identical neural mechanisms in our brains; the same excitatory sex centre in our limbic system and the same scattering of inhibitory centres in our cerebral hemispheres, which restrict and control our sexual behaviour. Things differ only because we choose to programme our inhibitory centres in different ways.

Children in the West are taught that they mustn't play with their genital organs. (This restriction was sometimes ignored by English nannies who found they could pacify their young charges by fondling their genitals.) Other races expect young boys to handle their penises as freely as they stroke their toes or scratch their ears.

The cultural variation in sexual taboos is vast. An American anthropologist discovered this a few years ago when she embarked on a field trip to Turkey accompanied by her eighteen-month-old daughter. She was assigned to an outlying country district where the peasant women encouraged her to follow their example and 'kiss and praise her daughter's genitals as a positive and motherly action'. To them this was natural; to the American anthropologist it was tantamount to child abuse.[9]

Similar variations exist in our acceptance of nudity. Some races feel no shame in the sight of the naked human body; others have strict rules governing the parts which can and can't be shown. In eighteenth-century England it was considered indecent for a woman to expose her ankles, but not to reveal her breasts. Nowadays it is *de trop* to expose the nipples, but fashionable to display the legs. For many years in Japan it was thought indelicate to kiss in public, which is why the Japanese government banned the public display of Rodin's 'Kiss' on the grounds that it was obscene. Yet they held no taboos about men and women bathing together in the nude.

Some cultures take a totally permissive attitude towards sexual expression in childhood; others teach youngsters that sex is evil, disgusting and dirty. And therein lies our problem. We go through life in a state of conflict, an internal revolution in which the biological dos battle with the cultural don'ts. As children we are taught to conceal our bodies, repress our sexual feelings and keep away from members of the opposite sex. Then, when we reach maturity, we are suddenly expected to shed these restrictions and embark on an uninhibited, intimate relationship with one of these taboo individuals. No wonder some couples, when they enter the state of holy wedlock, find it so difficult to join together what society has so painstakingly kept asunder.

A young Scottish girl suffered this problem. She was brought up in a religious home where 'sex was never spoken of at all'. Her father disapproved of dancing, and so as a young teenager she was denied this way of getting to close quarters with the opposite sex. When she went to study at Munich University, she attended the wild, pre-Lenten *faschung* carnival, but didn't allow herself to get carried away by the beer-drinking and revelry. In a letter to her mother she reported that she was the only woman at the carnival who didn't get kissed. She'd dressed in sober clothes and maintained an icy demeanour, convinced that 'it would be a strange man that wanted to kiss a block of ice'. At twenty-four she had her first kiss, and found it 'quite horrible'. Five years later, still chaste and totally ignorant of sexual matters, she found a 'nice' man who respected her decency, and married him. Not surprisingly, the honeymoon was a disaster. So too were the months which followed, and after five years she got a divorce – still a virgin. That girl was Marie Stopes, who spent the remainder of her life campaigning for the sexual enlightenment of women. Her books were widely read, and her views widely supported, and yet they haven't killed the belief that girls can, and should, aim to be chaste virgins one minute and uninhibited lovers the next.

This is an unrealistic demand, and a sure recipe for disaster, as Rose, one of my patients, discovered. Like Marie Stopes, she had had a puritanical upbringing, and when she eventually married, it was to a 'nice' man, who hadn't made sexual advances like all the other boys she knew. Throughout the years of her marriage she told me of her sexual disappointments. Not once was their union consummated. Rose lost her virginity only in her seventies, some years after her husband's death, when she was seduced by her doctor. Not surprisingly, the long-awaited experience gave her not the slightest pleasure.

The behavioural psychologists will argue that since sexual taboos are *learned*, they can be *unlearned*. In substance this is true, but in practice it is not easy to overthrow long established cultural habits. Breaking old taboos is as easy, or difficult, as giving up smoking. It's feasible, but arduous. Yet it must be done if we are to achieve maturity and regain our freedom of sexual manoeuvre.

Bewitched, Bothered and Bewildered

Psychologists have known for some while that the finest way to overcome fears and phobias is by direct confrontation. If you can't stand the sight of spiders it's no good spending your life running away from them. That will only confirm your fear. To overcome your terror you've got to face them head-on. Look at them, picture them in your mind's eye, make drawings of them – maybe even festoon your bedroom with toy spiders on dangling strings. In this way the phobia can gradually be overcome for, as Ralph Waldo Emerson rightly claimed: 'Do the thing you fear and the death of fear is certain.'

34

So it is with long-standing inhibitions and sexual hang-ups. The more you observe them, the more firmly established they become. Now is the time to delve into your temporal lobes and examine your inherited store of sexual inhibitions and taboos. Which do you want to keep, and which to modify or destroy?

Do you have a hang-up about using 'obscene' language which you would like to change? A Melanesian tribesman can talk as freely about his penis as he can about his elbow. Can you? In any case, why are Anglo-Saxon words considered so very much more lewd than their Latin equivalents? Why are vagina and coitus acceptable, but cunt and fuck beyond the pale?

During the Second World War, a titled English lady visited a front-line casualty station in Egypt to bring comfort to the wounded troops. She came to one bed where a Cockney soldier was recovering from a groin injury which threatened his marital prospects. Seeing no sign of bandages or plaster casts she asked the man where he had been wounded. 'I can't tell you, Mum,' he replied, 'I don't speak no Latin.' What a ridiculous state of affairs. Pure balls – or should that be pure testicles? As an ancient Greek said, 'Man should not be ashamed to name what God has not been ashamed to create.'

A newspaper columnist can write f*** without causing offence, but cannot write the word in full. Are there still readers who need to be protected from this particular profanity? If so, are they so naïve that they cannot decipher the cryptic reference? And at what point are their sensibilities disturbed? Would they find **** preferable, and f**k doubly outrageous?

Consider also the taboos against nudity. Must you always wear clothes when you walk about the house? Are you too bashful to make love in full daylight? Must sex always be confined to a darkened room with the lights switched off? Can't it occasionally be in a meadow on a brilliant summer's day? If you regret being held back by such cultural shibboleths, change them. Make it clear that *you* are in firm control of your temporal lobes.

And what about masturbation? As a child you were probably told that it wasn't 'nice' to handle your genitals. Have you overcome this reticence? The Greeks regarded their sex organs with reverence, calling the female organs *aidon*, which means 'that which inspires holy awe'. Are you equally proud of your genitalia? Or do infantile inhibitions hold you back from fondling them, admiring them and using them as objects for your pleasure?

At school you might have been censured for looking at 'dirty' pictures. Is this ban still in force? Could you now relax and watch a blue movie without feeling embarrassment or shame? If not, the sex inhibitory centres of your brain have become your master rather than your slave.

At the University of New South Wales in Sydney, a team of psychiatrists and psychologists took a group of frigid women – known locally as chilly sheilas – and helped them to deal with their sexual apathy by gradually overcoming their deep-seated fears and inhibitions. First they introduced them to films of naked men. Once they had overcome their aversion to these photographs, they showed them 'more sophisticated hard-core pornography of women sexually aroused by men'. When the now not-so-chilly sheilas could handle these scenes without blanching, they progressed to watching films showing 'couples engaged in the sexual act in various states of ecstasy'. As a result of this deconditioning process, 70 per cent of the women lost their inhibitions and were able to enjoy a more richly rewarding sex life.[10]

Sexercise 3
Cleansing the Cellars

Sexual inhibitions are deeply embedded in our psyche. If they are allowed to persist unchallenged they can put a permanent dampener on our sex lives. This can be avoided by bringing them into the open and subjecting them to careful review.

Read the following checklist and see if you are unduly hamstrung by unnecessary inhibitions:

- *Nudity* Can you strip off for a medical examination, or expose your body on a nudist beach, without feeling embarrassment or shame?
- *Masturbation* Do you feel there is something indecent or unwholesome about sexual self-stimulation? Is it something you can do unself-consciously in the presence of your partner?
- *Sexual language* Can you talk and write freely about love-making, in sexually explicit language, especially with your partner?
- *Pornography* What is your response to blue movies and erotic passages in novels? Excitement, amusement, boredom – or disgust?
- *Oral sex* Do you find the whole concept of oral sex distasteful, or do you regard it as just another means of sexual communication and arousal?

When you have considered the list, decide which of the inhibitions and taboos you want to retain and which to modify or remove. The choice is yours, providing it does not cause conflict with your partner. If you don't fancy oral sex, don't make it part of your sexual repertoire. If, on the other hand, you decide that you no longer want to maintain a taboo on oral sex, set out consciously and deliberately to overcome this restriction by making a regular practice of fellatio and cunnilingus. Repeat the practice until it becomes as natural and wholesome as enjoying an ice lolly. Or, if you find yourself tongue-tied when talking about sexual matters, set out to open the channels of communication with your partner. You'll find your reticence will lessen if you discuss together your intimate feelings and needs.

In this way you will gradually overcome your burden of irrational fear and guilt and gain greater autonomy and control over your sexual behaviour. In doing so you will confirm the truth of Emerson's maxim, that by facing the things you fear, the death of fear is certain.

You Made Me Love You

Love is a passion which flourishes best in an environment of positively charged emotion. It thrives on laughter, good food, cheerful music and warm companionship, but withers if we allow ourselves to wallow in states of anger, anxiety, guilt or fear.

Dr Helen Kaplan believes that most cases of deficient libido stem from an active suppression of sexual desire. People 'make themselves angry, fearful or distracted, and so tap into the natural physiological inhibitory mechanisms which suppress sexual desire,' she reports.[11] Some switch off the fires of love by focusing on their partner's unattractive features: his pot belly and bad breath, her fat thighs and drooping breasts. Another 'turn-off' mechanism is to relive the partner's past misdemeanours, their isolated episodes of violence, neglect or infidelity. Another popular way of turning down the erotic thermostat is to provoke a fight. If she shows signs of getting amorous by loosening the top button of her new silk blouse when he wants to watch a sports programme on television, his easiest escape route is to pick a quarrel about her extravagance. This immediately brings the loving to an end. How could anyone expect him to make love to someone who has just squandered the housekeeping on a new silk blouse? Whatever the complaint, the result is the same. The mood switches from love to aggression. 'In physiological terms,' explains Kaplan, 'the sex circuits are blocked by the activity of the fear and "anger" circuits.'[12]

Other hang-ups stem from religious bigotry. God created us sexual beings and would hardly wish to deprive us of the joys of his creation. Yet the end result of Western religious teaching has often been to denigrate sex and create a guilt cult. The ancients worshipped at the shrines of Eros and Aphrodite, but we have been encouraged to bow down to the gods of celibacy and asceticism. Our female saints have all been virgins; our male saints invariably celibate.

In practice it has been accepted that sex should be permitted between married couples, but only providing it is for procreation rather than recreation. At no time should sex be enjoyed. St Jerome made this quite clear when he warned: 'He who too ardently loves his wife is an adulterer.' This must make the Seventh Commandment – 'Thou shalt not commit adultery' – the most frequently broken of all the ten Mosaic laws, with the possible exception of the tenth, which prohibits the coveting of your neighbour's wife.

Anyone who has come under the influence of the Christian religion must have absorbed some of these cultural inhibitions from childhood onwards. One small boy came home from school and told his parents that they had had a whole morning of sex instruction. 'First the vicar told us *why* we shouldn't. Then the doctor told us *how* we shouldn't and finally the headmaster told us *where* we shouldn't.'

Given this background it is no wonder that we often carry with us a burden of sexual guilt and shame. Are you a prisoner of the past? Who is in charge of *your* current sexual behaviour? Is it your parents, with the restrictions they imposed when you were young? Or is it your childhood mentors, teachers, godparents and priests?

Sexercise 4
The Inner Game

The medieval monks tried to remain chaste by keeping their minds free from sexually arousing thoughts. You should do the reverse, if you want to increase your level of sexual arousal. You should shift the balance from inhibition to stimulation by making a conscious effort to bombard your limbic system with every conceivable form of sensual stimulation. *Look* at erotic pictures, *listen* to erotic poetry and music, *read* erotic literature and, above all else, *think* sexy thoughts.

A survey carried out by the American Association for Marriage and Family Therapy revealed that 80 per cent of women and 97 per cent of men fantasise. Sometimes it's a complicated reverie – of bondage, masked strangers and group orgies – which lasts for several minutes. At other times it's a sexy thought about a neighbour which lasts no more than a few seconds. Whether long or short, these fantasies have the same effect: they increase our level of sexual arousal, sometimes to the point of triggering an actual climax. Toying with your imagination can be as sexually arousing as playing with your genitals. It is reckoned that one in three women have orgasms as a result of erotic dreams, and a much smaller percentage as a sequel to waking fantasies.

If you find it difficult to indulge in sexual daydreams, you can turn yourself on by sharing other people's fantasies. Some people may be shocked, but few totally unmoved, by reading the wide range of erotic fantasies included in Nancy Friday's anthologies *My Secret Garden* and *Men in Love*[13]. An alternative way of stimulating the brain's sex centres is to *write* an erotic short story or novelette. Then you'll discover that if you *think* sexy you'll *feel* sexy.

SUMMARY

- Eroticism is a state of mind rather than an affliction of the heart. A simple and effective way of stimulating the sex centres of your brain is to give free rein to your sexual fantasies and longings.
- Aim to feel comfortable with your naked body, for tests show that sexual satisfaction is less commonly reported in people who are unduly prudish and shy.
- Many adults carry with them a heavy burden of childhood inhibitions and taboos which prevent them from enjoying a rich sex life. Does this apply to you? If so, search the inhibitory centres of your brain and identify the inhibitions which are holding you back from achieving sexual fulfilment. Can you talk freely about your love life in sexually explicit language? Can you have a free and frank discussion with your partner about the things which turn you on? Do you feel reluctant to handle your genitals? Is masturbation naughty? Maintain whatever sexual mores you choose, but make sure that they are *your* standards, and not those handed down to you by your parents.
- Love is a passion which thrives in an atmosphere of positively charged emotion. So when you are with your lover, try to create an ambience of gaiety and warmth. Don't turn him or her off by giving way to feelings of anger, anxiety or guilt. Aim instead to create a mood of fun – good food, lively music, laughter and warm companionship.

Five

Give Me Five
Minutes More

Learning any skill takes time and effort, whether it's tennis, bridge or caber-tossing. Hosts of people want to increase their sex drive. Many will gladly pay for the latest aphrodisiac, or hormone rejuvenation treatment. But how many are prepared to *work* towards that goal? Are you? To be more specific, how much time are you prepared to devote to the sexercises in this book? Are you willing to give them as much time as you would to learning a foreign language or improving your golf swing? If not, it suggests that you place a higher priority on reducing your golf handicap than on achieving sexual happiness, which may, of course, be true.

Sex is the only performance we expect to excel at without knowledge, practice or experience. We wouldn't let a youngster take the wheel of a car without first taking driving lessons, so why do we send them out on life's highway without training in the erotic arts?

Infancy is the ideal time for giving the first lessons in the amatory arts. In Japan it is traditional for a young girl to be given a sex manual – called *The Woman's University* – on the eve of her wedding.[1] The books are expensively produced and beautifully illustrated, with paintings of couples engaging in oral sex or locked in unusual coital positions. But isn't it rather late to be teaching a girl the facts of life a few hours before she embarks on her honeymoon?

Animals, and most tribal races, learn about sex the natural way: by observation and experimentation during childhood. Bruno Bettelheim, in his study of worldwide puberty rites, *Symbolic Wounds*, contrasts the repressive upbringing of American children with the freedom offered to Aboriginal children. In the Australian heartland, 'children are allowed to indulge sexual desires without criticism', he writes. 'They may be invited by a mother, older brother or sister, or some other person, to have sexual intercourse with an adult or a child of the same age standing nearby. Their sexual organs may be played with . . . At an early age they learn of the sexual act by direct observation, and they imitate sexual activities among themselves, publicly when they are young and

40

somewhat more privately when they become older and more self-conscious.'[2] This level of freedom is more easily maintained in a small, close-knit community, where behaviour can be closely monitored to ensure that sexual licence does not degenerate into sexual abuse.

How different from the upbringing of *our* children, whom we try to shield from all forms of sexual expression. We may give them a theoretical, and highly romanticised, introduction to the mating habits of the birds and bees, but we're none too happy if they actually see a dog mounting a bitch, in case it stimulates their exploratory instinct. Unlike the Australian Aborigines, we try to shield our youngsters from scenes of flagrant sex. Like Noël Coward, who was taking one of his young godchildren for a walk when they came across two dogs mating. 'What are they doing, Uncle?' the young boy asked.

'Oh!' said Coward without a moment's pause, 'one of the poor doggies has gone blind and the other is pushing him all the way to St Dunstan's.'

This prudery is potentially dangerous, for infants learn by imitating adult behaviour. This is as true of copulation as it is of cooking, cursing or clay pigeon shooting. When Professor Harry Harlow carried out his studies of Rhesus monkeys he found that male infants who had no adult behaviour to copy during their formative years grew up with a complete lack of sexual know-how. As a result of this ignorance, when they were first introduced to a mate they would often attempt to mount her head or flank rather than her rump. Others showed an almost total lack of sexual interest. 'The unhappy beasts sat about morosely,' Harlow noted, 'staring vacantly into space now and then, as if in sheer frustration, biting and tearing their own arms.'[3]

Children start to show an interest in the opposite sex from about the age of eight onwards. Yet most human youngsters are encouraged to grow up as inexperienced as Harlow's socially deprived Rhesus monkeys. They reach their teens without ever having seen an adult copulating, except perhaps in pornographic films and magazines. Still more remarkable, many grown-up children have never seen their parents kissing, cuddling and fondling. As a result they often find it difficult to regard their parents as sexual beings, with passions like their own.

Most parents accept the idea of sex education in schools, providing the subject is treated scientifically and doesn't involve homework. Some years ago I was banned from speaking on the BBC because hundreds of angry parents had written in complaining that I was guilty of trying to corrupt the innocence of British youth. My crime? I had talked about birth control at a time when impressionable teenagers might be listening. Some days earlier the papers had carried sensational reports of

41

teenage abortions and schoolgirl mothers. Yet it was thought irresponsible to talk to youngsters about sexual matters. At about the same time the Health Education Council received a letter from a young wife who had heard about the withdrawal method of contraception and wanted to know how she could obtain it. Such was the level of ignorance at the time, yet the guardians of the nation's morals still thought it essential to protect children from all forms of sexual enlightenment.

Boom Bang-a-Bang

A repressive childhood training makes some people so ashamed of sex that they either want to dispense with it altogether or get it over as quickly as possible. Some young men want to come before they've arrived. They can climax quicker than you can say 'wham-bang-thank-you-mam'. This is true bestial sex, a coupling almost as quick as that of the gerenuks, the exquisite African antelopes who can mate on the hoof without even breaking the rhythm of their stride. Equally brisk are the whales and dolphins, who can achieve face-to-face sexual union in a few split seconds while they are leaping out of the water.

Humans take far longer to achieve a necessary state of sexual arousal. This is one of the features which most clearly differentiates the sexual behaviour of animals and that of man. We have to spend a long while in pre-copulatory foreplay, kissing, cuddling and caressing, before we reach an optimum level of sexual arousal. For a monkey the whole cycle of sexual union is over in seconds. For them, as for other animals, the sole purpose of sex is the perpetuation of the species. For man it serves the double function of procreation and pair bonding. The first can be achieved in seconds. The second takes far longer.

It is traditional for couples in the Orient to devote a long time to the process of sensual arousal. Some *yogis* recommend that lovers should lie in each other's arms for an hour without moving. We are part of a far more frenzied culture. We make a virtue of haste. We live in an age of fast cars, fast food and fast sex. We like quick solutions and favour books which offer rapid results, like *The One-Minute Manager* and *The One-Minute Parent*. (At any minute now I'm expecting to receive a review copy of *The Thirty-Second Lover*.)

Love can't be hurried, especially for women, who invariably take longer to become sexually aroused than men. Many Western males are not prepared to grant them that time. Men frequently suffer from premature ejaculation, but I've never heard a woman complain that she came too soon. Her most common gripe is that love-making is so rushed that she is not adequately aroused before coitus starts and so she is unprepared to reach an orgasm.

This was Deirdre's problem. She told her sex therapist that she did not know what had happened to her wonderful Latin lover. 'Michael used to be incredible. He could make love for an hour just to my *toe*, for God's sake, and I'd tingle all over. Then we got married and he suddenly becomes this sexual robot. Groan, squirt, and that's all.'[4]

Sexual arousal takes time. The natives of Bali believe that hasty sex causes deformed babies, a myth which would have some substance if it were modified into the more realistic belief that hasty sex causes deformed relationships.

So Near and Yet So Far

To reach the peak of sexual arousal takes time, and also a measure of concentration. We lead such crowded lives that we often find it difficult to give love-making our undivided attention, even for a few minutes. In fact it's said that the main advantage of the rear-entry coital position is that it allows both partners to watch television at the same time!

Ours is a grasshopper culture which fosters grasshopper minds. Our thought processes are transient and ephemeral. Unlike Buddhists, who live in the eternal present, we try to live in the ever-changing here and then, how soon and when.

One of the doors to success – in sex as in life itself – is marked 'Concentration'. Inventors have a reputation for being scatter-brained and forgetful, simply because their minds are so focused on their work that they lose awareness of everything else. The dedicated professor isn't absentminded; he's present-minded somewhere else.

Zen Buddhists are trained to focus all their powers on the task they're doing, whether it's archery, motorcycle maintenance or boiling a pan of rice. So it should be with sex. When you're love-making there should be no room for any extraneous feelings or thoughts. Everything should be focused on the appreciation of the sensual here and now. There should be no thought of past sexual failures, parental warnings or social taboos and expectations. The passing moment is virgin time and space, a *tabula rasa* on which we are completely free to write whatever we choose.

Loving-making is an experience to enjoy, not a tool to be manipulated for personal gain. It *is* the goal, not the means by which we achieve the goal. So many people have sex for purely egotistical reasons. They seek a release from nervous tension. They want reassurance that they are lovable or sexy. They need friendship. They want to exercise power, make emotional demands, settle a debt or return a favour.

These selfish demands act as barriers to unconditional loving and impair the depth and richness of the erotic experience. This has been the experience of New York sex therapist Jerry Gillies, who writes: 'In conducting hundreds of workshops on love and relationships, I have found that those men and women who have moved towards eliminating demands, conditions and expectations from their relationships have longer-lasting and more intense love experiences.'[5]

You're My Everything

In a loving relationship you should be prepared to dispense with all egocentric preconditions and simply love and let love. Our entire focus should be on the sensations flooding into our limbic system – the touch of flesh on flesh, the delicate body perfumes, the loving glances, the words of endearment, the rhythm of muscular movements, the warmth, the changing breath sounds and the gradually quickening pulsing of the heart. That is the way to heighten sexual arousal.

Our brains are constantly bombarded by sensory stimulation. A confusing barrage of sounds, sights, smells and feelings so great that it cannot all be registered. To prevent sensory overload, we have to be selective in our data processing. We have to concentrate on the information we want to receive and filter out the irrelevant 'noise'. The choice is ours. We determine the focus of our attention, and decide what is relevant and what is superfluous in our sensory environment.

If we're making love, we have the power to determine whether we focus our attention on the radio or on the erotic sensations arising from our bodies. The switch is easily made; the outcome dramatically different.

At present you are consciously aware of only a small fraction of the stimuli reaching your brain. Many other sensations go totally unrecorded. This I can change, even though you may be several thousand miles away while you're reading this book. I may now be pottering in my garden in the heartland of England, while you are sitting in your lounge in Sydney, Singapore or San Francisco. Yet I'm going to influence, not your thoughts, but your actual physical feelings. A few seconds ago you were unaware that your buttocks were being compressed by the chair on which you're sitting. But, hey presto! Now that I've brought it to your attention you have begun to notice the sensations emanating from your seat. How easy it is! By making a simple shift of mental focus sensations can be either suppressed or brought to light.

This is how Boris Zolotov, the Russian faith healer, exerts his influence over the ladies in his audience. He brings them to a high pitch of sexual arousal simply by making them aware of their sexual desires and feelings.

Whenever you want to make love – whether you're lying in bed, sitting on the sofa or rolling in the hay – make sure that each of your five senses is totally committed to the job in hand. Wherever you are, be there. Don't allow yourself to be in vacant possession of your body.

You'll find this is far more difficult than you imagine. People learning to meditate, possibly by gazing at a candle flame, find it difficult to stop their thoughts wandering. This they are taught to expect. Outside thoughts, distractions and irrelevant daydreams will always intrude when you try to focus on a particular task. The only remedy is to bring your thoughts back repeatedly to the job in hand.

Zen Buddhists learn this skill early in their training. A pupil asked his Zen master the fundamental question: 'What is the way?'

'Your everyday mind,' the master replied. 'When I am hungry, I eat; when I am tired, I sleep.'

'Isn't this what everyone does?' the student asked.

'No,' the master explained. 'Most people are never totally in what they are doing; when eating, they may be absentmindedly preoccupied with a thousand different thoughts; when sleeping their dreams may keep them agitated throughout the night. The supreme state of the thoroughly integrated person is to be without a divided mind.'

All or Nothing at All

Many people find it difficult to allow themselves to be totally sensual. It runs counter to their training. Educated people are taught to live in their brains, not in their bodies. Yet the marriage service says: 'With my body I thee worship.' Does this mean that kissing, cuddling and sexual caressing are sacramental acts?

The Rev. Donald Reeves, Rector of St James's Church, London, has no doubt that this is so. 'Eroticism,' he writes, 'should have a central place in the celebration and rituals of the church.'[6]

The Christian church is slowly accepting this view, which has been the very cornerstone of many of the new religious cults.

When the Bhagwan Shree Rajneesh set up his ashram in Poona he quickly became known as the 'love guru'. His disciples, or *sannyasins*, were encouraged to develop their eroticism. When they made love, they were told that they were 'orchestrating' their energies and generating a

45

power and sexual dynamism which would be transformed into wisdom and love. The Bhagwan himself had no time for the Indian tradition of ascetic fakirs and holy celibates. He loved his comforts and he enjoyed his sex, claiming that he had 'had more women than any man in history'.[7] (The young girls who administered to his needs knew better and reported that, owing to his asthma and bad back, the Bhagwan could cope with nothing more energetic than a quick blow job.)

Many people considered the Bhagwan an evil influence; a licentious sexual reprobate. But he did help his followers overcome their sexual inhibitions and develop a more wholesome acceptance of their sexuality. He taught them that sexual exuberance is not only permissible, but positively desirable. His own lust for life was infectious. He was an outrageous hedonist, who did not think it strange that a holy man should keep a stable of ninety-three Rolls-Royce cars for his personal enjoyment. This was no embarrassment for him, and he got great delight from the sticker on his car which proclaimed: 'Jesus saves, Moses invests, Bhagwan spends.'

Sex can never be made an intellectual pursuit. We need to surrender to our feelings if we are to get full enjoyment from our love-making. This point was aptly made by the old Indian adage: 'You can't taste the honey by licking the pot.' Similar advice was given by Fritz Perls, one of the founding fathers of the Encounter Group movement, who told his followers: 'Lose your mind and come to your senses.'

Magic Moments

Throughout the ages people have been using love magic to enchant the person of their dreams. The procedures, whether used by an ancient Egyptian slave or a modern Trobriand islander, are remarkably similar. First an item closely associated with the person is obtained, such as a lock of hair, a piece of clothing, a wax image or a sample of soil on which his or her feet have trod. This memento is then used as a focus of meditation, often while mystic spells and chants are made.

Some love magic requires the collection of samples of the loved one's pubic hair. (It might be thought that anyone close enough to do this has no need of supernatural aid to help them in their wooing!) Nail clippings are another frequently recommended ingredient of ancient love charms. (The Koran advises Muslims to bury their nail clippings so that they can't fall into the hands of black magicians.)

The universal employment of sex magic, and its long history, suggests that it *is* a potent force. If this is so, how does it work? Modern research workers discount the idea that the power emanates from supernatural agencies. The phenomenon can be explained quite simply on the basis of applied thought control. 'Enchantment is merely ritualised mesmerism,' is one investigator's interpretation.[7]

Nowadays, sufferers from cancer are encouraged to use visualisation techniques to stimulate their defence systems. Sometimes they are advised to imagine that their white blood cells are soldiers, travelling round the body killing off the rogue cancer cells. Sex magic employs a similar process.

Sexercise 5
Love Magic

Take some object which you closely associate with your soul-mate. This can be a lock of their pubic hair, if you fancy erotic exotica, or a portrait photograph if you are of a more practical nature. Put this token by your bed or in your wallet or handbag, and dwell on it lovingly and longingly whenever you get the chance. Use it regularly as a focus for your erotic desires and thoughts.

A modern magician, who writes under the soubriquet 'Father Sabazius', describes the principle of the exercise as follows: 'One should seek to visualise the subject more and more . . . and should see, "feel", and "hold" him, quite naturally, up to the point when one wonders if he is actually close at hand. The intensity of concentration should be constantly maintained calmly, precisely and naturally.'[8]

Follow this exercise regularly and you will increase your level of sexual arousal, especially for the person on whom you have been focusing. For, in the words of a famous French occult healer, 'No love can resist magic . . . Willpower, dynamic force, and concentrated thought bring extraordinary results.' With this last statement, few doctors or psychologists would disagree.

SUMMARY
- Allow yourself time to love. The great pleasures of life cannot be hurried. This is as true of sex as it is of eating a gourmet meal or listening to a Beethoven symphony.
- When you're making love, banish from your mind all extraneous thoughts and feelings. Don't worry about the jobs you've got to do, the noise of the creaking bedsprings or the strange pain in your right

shoulder. Simply concentrate your attention on enjoying the sensuous pleasures of the 'here and now' – the touch of flesh on flesh, the delicate body perfumes, the warmth, the rhythm of your muscular movements.

- Never allow your love-making to become an intellectual exercise – a search for mythical G-spots or a striving for multiple orgasms or simultaneous climaxes. To enjoy the heights of sexual arousal follow the advice of Fritz Perls: 'Lose your mind and come to your senses.'
- If you want to increase your affection for a particular person, harness the ancient forces of sex magic which derive their power from a process of fascination or concentrated thought control. Obtain a symbolic token of the person you desire – a photograph, handkerchief or lock of hair – and use this regularly as a focus for your erotic thoughts and desires.

Six

Enjoy Yourself, It's Later Than You Think

All animals are pleasure seekers. Even a simple creature like the amoeba organises its life on strictly hedonic principles. If a stimulus is pleasant, like food or gentle warmth, it moves towards it. If it is noxious, like a chemical poison or an excessively bright light, it gives it a wide berth. By this simple motivational system even the simplest blob of protoplasm is encouraged to act in ways which help to ensure its survival.

The same behavioural inducements occur throughout the animal kingdom. A gorilla receives a pleasure bonus if it copulates or empties an over-full bladder, but suffers pain if it touches a burning log or eats a bunch of mouldy bananas. In this way it is encouraged to act in ways which ensure its long-term good.

The pursuit of pleasure is an exceedingly powerful motivating force. This was first demonstrated by psychologist James Olds, who discovered that laboratory rats experience extreme 'pleasure' when certain regions of their brain are subjected to electrical stimulation. To examine the phenomenon in greater depth, Dr Olds placed electrodes on their pleasure centres and connected them to a simple on-off lever which the rats could operate for themselves. As soon as the animals realised that they could turn themselves on by operating the switch, they gave up all thoughts of anything else. Eating, sleeping and drinking were forgotten in their frenzy to get the electric thrill, which they sometimes induced several thousand times an hour.[1]

Similar experiments have been carried out with fish, guinea pigs, rabbits, cats, dogs, dolphins and monkeys, which show that the pursuit of pleasure is a widespread animal preoccupation. But what about man? We have the wealth, skills and technical resources to devote our whole lives to a never-ending pursuit of self-gratification. Instead we often opt to pursue other goals. Eating is delightful, yet many women repeatedly suffer hunger pangs to keep themselves fashionably slim. Reading a book on a Saturday afternoon is an innocent source of fun, but some men seem to prefer the pains and rigours of a marathon race. Time and again we give up the pleasures of the moment for the doubtful recompense of future benefits – job promotions, larger incomes or increased status. Psychologists call this strange aberration 'deferred gratification'. In practice it means jam yesterday, jam tomorrow, but never jam today. No wonder, in our anxious, work-weary world, that we look with such envy on the simple, hedonistic lifestyle of tribal peoples.

Ain't We Got Fun

The Talmud asserted that it was a Jew's *duty* to take pleasure from the good things in life. Otherwise, it warned, he might be judged guilty of failing to live in accordance with natural law. 'In the world to come each of us will be called to account for the good things God put on earth which we refused to enjoy.' This Talmudic injunction no doubt applies to sex as well as to smoked salmon sandwiches and gefilte fish.

Two thousand years ago this philosophy suffered a dramatic change when the leaders of the Jewish and newly emerging Christian faiths placed a curb on physical pleasures. According to Josephus, the early Jewish historian, the Essene sect 'reject pleasure as evil, but esteem continence and the conquest of our passions to be virtue'. Before this time rabbis held that celibacy was a sin; now in some circles it became praiseworthy to be a virgin or eunuch.

The early Christian church, under its twin, celibate leaders Jesus of Nazareth and Paul of Tarsus, adopted a similar anti-erotic stance. So the guilt cult spread, reaching its zenith under the Puritans, who made it iniquitous to do anything which brought a blush to the cheeks or a smile to the lips. They were the sort of people who would ban bull-fighting, not because it causes the bull pain, but because it gives the spectators pleasure.

Christian missionaries travelled the globe trying to spread the glad and good news. In one hand they brought the good tidings of altruistic Christian love; in the other a scourge with which they tried to suppress the natives' natural eroticism. Nudity was shameful, fertility dances obscene, abandoned sexuality an unpardonable vice. In some areas the outward expression of the sexual urge was suppressed, but it was never totally quenched. When one missionary, during a hell-fire sermon, told his African congregation that there were seventy-nine separate sexual sins, he had scores of requests for a detailed list.

This ambivalence still persists today, judging by the graffiti on a poster outside a London church. The poster told passers-by: 'If you are tired of sin come and join our Sunday service.' Underneath someone had scrawled: 'But if you are not, phone 071 612 3022. (If this proves to be a genuine phone number I apologise, and wish to make clear that neither the author nor the publisher of this book can be held responsible for any encounters which may ensue.)

We may try to live ascetic lives, but the drive for pleasure is never far away. Sex is at the forefront of this primordial pleasure quest. This is generally recognised, but what is less well appreciated is that sexual vitality is in many ways a by-product of the hedonistic lifestyle. Anyone who tries to kill joy destroys the very well-spring of sexuality.

Spread a Little Happiness

The Puritans were astute when they set out to promote the virtues of self-denial and hard work. They realised that moralising and hell-fire sermons couldn't halt the people's search for pleasure, but fancied that they could be made incapable of debauchery if their noses were fastened to the grindstone and their shoulders pinioned to the wheel. How could a man embark on a night's carousing if he had just spent a twelve-hour day toiling on a farm or working in a 'dark, satanic mill'?

Preachers found sexual restraint difficult to sell, so they switched their marketing campaign and offered an alternative product – self-advancement. People could better themselves through industry, discipline and self-restraint. Deferred gratification was the means by which they could attain success, wealth and social status. They might suffer a little on the way, and miss out on some of life's immediate goodies, but it would be worth it in the end.

Even politicians and philosophers joined the theologians on the deferred gratification bandwagon. All three promised the proletarian masses that their current miserable existences of hardship, toil, strife and self-abnegation would eventually be rewarded. For the theologian the reward was heaven; for the politician a fairer society; for the philosopher a Utopian world. 'Pie in the sky when you die', was their general promise. But should we be prepared to wait that long? As Muhammad Ali said, he wanted his slice of pie now, 'on the ground, when I'm still around'.

Many people today accept the principle of deferred gratification without question. They work long hours, which leaves little time for leisure and even less for personal enjoyment. Some struggle to retain their jobs, others to pay their monthly mortgages, rent and food bills. But many others over-exert themselves in the belief that they are investing in the future. But the only time you can enjoy yourself is *now*.

Our bodies should be instruments of pleasure rather than implements of toil. Whatever your long-term aspirations, if you want to enjoy a lively sex life, you must not allow the pleasure principle to be wholly supplanted by the work ethic.

Psychiatrists recognise a state of 'free-floating anxiety', a condition in which a generalised state of nervousness exists with no obvious cause. When we are in such a mood, everything that happens tends to give us cause for further worry and concern. To avoid this morbid condition, we need to create a world of 'free-floating happiness' and look at things through rose-tinted spectacles. This is when we are most likely to find happiness and experience sexual delight.

It's Foolish but it's Fun

'It is a sad fact that man does not live for pleasure alone,' said Albert Einstein. People often feel guilty if they admit to doing things which give them pleasure. They believe that, because it feels so good, it must be wicked to linger over a gourmet meal, bask idly in the sun, have a sensuous body massage or make love. The Epicurean Greek philosophers thought otherwise. They regarded these activities as morally good, *because* they gave pleasure.

Philosophers nowadays attract little public interest or support. Their theories are so abstruse that they bear no relationship to the interests and cares of everyday life. But this was not so 2,000 years ago when Epicurus argued that the purpose of philosophy was practical – to secure a happy life. Starting with this yardstick the Epicureans argued that pleasure was the natural and instinctive object of man's behaviour. 'We say that pleasure is the beginning and end of living happily,' Epicurus explained in a letter to a friend. As expounded by the Greek hedonic philosophers, this simple outlook brought immediate rewards as well as long-term social and altruistic benefits.

That Certain Feeling

Everyone can differentiate between pleasurable feelings and disagreeable feelings. But what exactly does this dichotomy entail? Sixty years ago psychologists suggested that we responded rather like the humble amoeba, in that the primary effect of pleasant sensations was to draw us towards the source of the stimulus, whereas unpleasant feelings tended to drive us away.[2]

This observation is directly relevant to sexual behaviour. When our loving is pleasant we are drawn towards our mate and encouraged to repeat the experience. When the loving proves distasteful we are repelled. Every sexual encounter is recorded in our memory stores. Every act is of significance, an experience which trains our sexual behaviour as surely as a ringing bell conditioned the salivary responses of Pavlov's dogs.

If our loving ends in failure or emotional humiliation, we tend to fight shy of it in future. If it brings us pleasure, we are motivated to repeat the experience. And the more we replicate this joyful feeling, the greater our sexual appetite becomes. This was why the Puritans wanted to curb erotic pleasure, because they knew that in doing so they would dampen sexual drive.

Laboratory experiments have shown the strength of this conditioning. Trials carried out at the University of Maryland have revealed that dogs which have been affectionately trained will cheerfully cross an electrified grid to be reunited with their owners and get a rewarding dose of petting and fondling.[3] This points the way to a highly effective way of keeping a spouse from straying. Faithfulness is best ensured, not by issuing jealous threats, but by supplying regular doses of love. Nagging will only drive partners away, but a daily ration of affection will have them crossing electrified grids and leaping through burning hoops to get back into their lover's arms.

Psychological studies have revealed a second major difference between pleasant and unpleasant feelings. The former are accompanied by physical relaxation, the latter by tension.[4] When we laugh, our muscles soften. When we become angry, they grow taut. When we listen to peaceful music, our stress hormone levels fall. When we watch a disturbing film, the levels of catecholamines rise. These bodily changes alter the response of the body to erotic stimulation in a way which makes pleasure the precursor of erotic arousal as well as its obvious, and delightful aftermath.

Let There be Love

Physiologists, like psychologists, have reason to believe that pleasure is conducive to love-making. They have drawn attention to the fact that the brain's sex centre is located very close to the pleasure centre, in the outside rim of the brain stem. This area, generally known as the limbic system, is one of the oldest parts of the human brain. It is present in primitive vertebrate animals in much the same form as it is in man. Its duty is to organise those functions which safeguard the survival of the individual and the perpetuation of the species, such as pleasure, pain, anger, 'fight and flight' and sexual reproduction.

Because of their close proximity, it seems highly likely that any activation of the pleasure centre brings about a simultaneous stimulation of the sex centre. (The same argument could be used to explain the common association between pleasure and pain, and between eroticism and painful stimulation, such as beatings, love bites and sadomasochism.)

Some physiologists believe that pleasure is experienced as a result of the release of endorphins, neurochemicals generated within the body which have a morphine-like action. This theory is supported by studies, carried out under carefully controlled, humane conditions, which show that the endorphin concentrations in the brains of laboratory rats are raised when they drink alcohol or copulate.[5] If the same is true of humans, as seems likely, it is not surprising that we should feel euphoric and a trifle drowsy after making love, since our limbic systems then are likely to be flooded with endorphins.

I'm in the Mood For Love

You'll enjoy sex more when you're in a happy frame of mind. If you don't feel sexy when your partner gives you the come-on signals, don't just do your duty unenthusiastically. Cheer yourself up first. Relax. Pamper yourself. Have a good meal with a bottle of wine. Listen to some romantic music. This will increase your level of arousal by getting the endorphins flowing to your limbic system. And the more aroused you are, the greater pleasure you'll get from the act of sex itself. This was proved by Barbara Hutton, a New York psychotherapist, who quizzed a large group of women about their sexual experiences. She discovered that women who said: 'I think about the pleasure I am receiving' almost every time they had intercourse, generally had an orgasm, whereas those who were less pleasure-focused had much poorer chances of reaching a climax.[6]

Whatever your religious training, or obsession with work, you must find time to savour life's pleasures if you want to enjoy a rich and satisfying sex life. A religious bigot scribbled on a wall 'Sex Kills'. Underneath someone added: 'Die happy!' This is the attitude to adopt. Our aim should be to follow the edict of Epicurus and 'Live happy!' Sex shouldn't be a serious business. The ancient Egyptians set a splendid example in this respect. They had a fun god called Res, whose image often hung over their beds to remind them that sex was play rather than marital obligation or mechanical ritual. Let's stress the giggles rather than the grunts and orgiastic groans. Our responsibility is to see that our partners have fun, both in and out of bed. After all, as Epicurus wrote, 'Pleasure is the beginning and end of living happily.'

Too Darn Hot

Heat has long been recognised as an aid to sexual arousal. Passions are aroused by warmth. Holiday romances blossom on the sun-warmed beaches of Bermuda, not during treks through the frozen wastes of Iceland or Alaska. Marie Stopes, the champion of women's sexual rights, was a great advocate of nude 'fire baths'. These she took in front of a roaring coal fire with her young guardsman lover, to help stimulate their sex drive.[7]

Both the male and female genitalia become suffused with blood during the early stages of sexual arousal. Perhaps we accentuate this process when we warm our nether regions. Many women masturbate by directing a stream of warm water onto their labia and clitoris. 'I lie in the tub on my back with a stream of very warm water on my vagina, mons and clitoris,' one woman told Shere Hite. 'The harder the pressure and the hotter the water, the quicker the orgasm.'[8]

Men have used a similar technique to increase their potency, sometimes increasing the blood flow to their genitals by rubbing them with counter-irritant creams, ground pepper or bunches of stinging nettles. This was a favourite cure for impotence in Roman times. Petronius, in his famous novel *The Satyricon*, tells how his hero Encolpius receives advances from a beautiful blonde but is ashamed to find that he is incapable of rising to the occasion. In search of an immediate cure, he consults a witch, who anoints his loins with ground pepper and lashes his belly with stinging nettles.

At other times men have used wire brushes and acids to raise blisters on the skin around their upper thighs. These aids to sexual arousal were once so popular that eighteenth-century French brothels provided them for the benefit of customers with potency problems in specially equipped rooms called *salles de preparation*.

Sex shops today offer a number of similar remedies, all designed to imitate the physiological feeling and appearance of genital arousal. One, called 'Love Foam', looks rather like shaving cream and is claimed to give the body 'a magical glow'. Another, called 'Orgy Butter', is advertised as a 'red, warm body rub' which 'gives a slippery, sensual effect'.

But possibly the simplest way of genital vasodilation is to take a warm bath. Dr Theodoor Van de Velde, the Dutch gynaecologist who wrote one of the first explicit sex manuals – the highly successful *Ideal Marriage* – recommends this as a cure for sexual anaesthesia in women and for men whose 'normal desires are impaired by slight languor and lassitude'.[9] He advised his patients to take a warm sitz bath as an immediate prelude to intercourse, to stimulate their pelvic and genital areas. A similar effect can be achieved with a warm hot-water bottle, providing it is not so warm that it scalds the flesh. (Judging by the number of women who carry a tell-tale mottling of their groin and upper thighs, this is not an uncommon way of rousing the sleeping goddess Kundalini.)

Some women also claim that they can excite their mates by reddening their backsides with heat, or with a light application of rouge. If this is true, its effect is likely to be achieved by the activation of an atavistic signalling mechanism. When female monkeys are on heat they develop a swollen, red rump which they display to let the male members of the troop know that they are ready and eager to be mounted. (This mammalian throwback may also explain why men sometimes take delight in pinching and slapping the female behind. This often occurs in courtship and pre-copulatory sex play, possibly because it reddens the flesh and provokes the enticing mounting symbol.)

History records that warm bathing has always been associated with sexual arousal. The Roman baths became notorious for their licentiousness, so much so that the Emperor Hadrian had to impose a ban on mixed bathing. Later European baths suffered a similar decline, the words 'stew' and 'bagnio' coming to be accepted synonyms for brothel. Casanova, on his travels, visited a London bagnio to broil in the warm water and then to dally with a courtesan. 'It makes a magnificent debauch,' he reported, 'and costs only six guineas.'

Georgian dandies and society ladies went to Bath to pursue their amorous interests. 'Here is performed all the wanton dalliances imaginable,' reported one writer. In the thermal waters total strangers fondled one another intimately, by what he described as 'accidental design'. Exactly what went on he was too coy to describe, believing that 'where the water concealed, so ought my pen'.[10]

The Christian church naturally forbade mixed bathing. For many years it considered even solitary bathing a vice, because of its tendency to lead to a surge of carnal desire. As a result many unwashed holy men became riddled with vermin. St Francis of Assisi was covered with lice, and when the martyred Thomas à Becket lay on his funeral pyre the vermin crawled out of his clothing as his body cooled, which pilgrims took as definite proof of his piety.

Sexercise 6
The Hedonic Bath

A hot bath is one simple way of stimulating your pleasure centres. For maximum effectiveness this should be taken in company, with aromatic herbs to excite your olfactory nerve endings and a final overall body massage to send a further tingle to the sex centres in the brain's limbic area.

You'll find that sharing a hot bath is one of the quickest ways of getting acquainted. It's an ideal ice-breaker, a splendid way of turning a frosty relationship into a warm friendship. This was discovered in Japan when a hotel built a large, warm pool where teenagers could get acquainted more quickly than on the disco floor. They called it *o-miai-furo*, or 'dating in the tub'. Within weeks of opening this novel courting-ground several youngsters had become engaged and the hotel had doubled its turnover.

The Japanese do not use soap in their communal baths, but you're not tied to such restrictions. So make a great feature of lathering each other's bodies with soap.

Afterwards, when your bodies are soft and warm, give each other a sensuous top-to-toe massage, choosing whatever oils you both prefer. The oils believed to have aphrodisiac properties are clary, jasmine, rose and ylang-ylang.

Clary, a member of the sage family with small blue flowers, exerts a euphoric effect and has been applied for many years to treat sexual debility. (Nicholas Culpeper, in his *British Herbal*, claims that taking clary leaves in wine 'provoketh venery'.) Jasmine is often used in body oils and, according to a leading British aromatherapist, has the effect of warming the genital organs, which makes it 'a great asset in treating impotence or frigidity'.[11] The erotic reputation of the rose is even older. The Greeks believed that the first rose grew from the blood of Adonis, and the Turks that it sprang from the blood of Venus. According to Marguerite Maury, the eminent aromatherapist, the rose has definite aphrodisiac properties and exerts a 'considerable influence on the female sexual organs'.[12]

Ylang-ylang, the least well known of all the 'aphrodisiac' aromatic oils, is obtained from the yellow flowers of a tall tree which grows in the Far Eastern rainforests. It has an exotic perfume and is said to allay frustration as well as stimulate desire.

These, then, are the basic ingredients of the Hedonic Bath, which should be taken in a leisurely, sensuous fashion: warmth, intimacy, alluring scents, nudity and shared physical contact. This heady cocktail of sensory stimuli can't fail to raise the level of arousal of the brain's sex centres.

SUMMARY

- Man is by nature a pleasure-seeking animal, so whatever you do in the name of sex make sure it gives you the maximum possible pleasure. Don't allow your joy to be curtailed by guilt feelings. The Puritans were wrong. You have a divine duty and right to enjoy the pleasures of life.
- Don't let your search for long-term goals – wealth, status or success – mar your enjoyment of the passing moment. Deferred gratification has its advocates, but you want some of your jam today as well as in the distant hereafter. The only time to enjoy sex is *now*.
- The pleasure centres of the brain are located close to the sex centres. This may explain why we feel sexy when we are pleasurably aroused. You'll increase your sex drive if you follow the command of Epicurus and 'Live happy!'
- Heat increases the blood flow to the male and female sex organs and has long been advocated as an aid to sexual arousal. To get you in the mood for love, take a long, lingering bath with your partner and follow it up with a top-to-toe body massage with aromatic oils.

Seven

Soft Lights and Sweet Music

Every animal is able to respond to external stimuli. This responsiveness is vital to their continuing existence. A gentle rustle in the bushes, suggesting the approach of a predator, and a vulnerable creature takes flight. A whiff of sex attractant chemical, released by a mate possibly furlongs away, and its sexual instincts are immediately aroused. Control the sensory input and it's possible to dictate the behavioural response.

This was the simple principle that underlined the teaching of the early behavioural psychologists. Pavlov had shown that dogs could be trained to salivate whenever they heard a bell ring. The behaviourists – led by John Watson and B.F. Skinner – believed that man could be submitted to the same conditioning process. We are no more than machines, they claimed, controlled by the sensory strings which operate our driving wheels. We do not act; we merely react to changes in our environment.

Aldous Huxley regarded this as a frightening prospect. If the behaviourists' theories were true, our behaviour could be manipulated by an unscrupulous government, a fate which formed the scenario of his apocalyptic book *Brave New World*. George Orwell contemplated the same dreadful possibilities in *1984*. In this gloomy tale of totalitarian ruthlessness, the Thought Police employ the techniques of classical Pavlovian conditioning to manipulate the proletariat. Even the people's love lives are subjected to state control. When Winston and Julia, two workers from the Ministry of Truth, develop an old-fashioned bourgeois passion for each other, the state sets out to subvert their love. Winston is taken to the Ministry of Love, where he is brainwashed to forget Julia and develop a substitute passion for the arch-dictator Big Brother.

In Orwell's mind, human eroticism could be manipulated as easily as the salivary flow of Pavlov's dogs. He was encouraged in this belief by the radical behaviourists who claimed that human behaviour could be explained by a simple S-R formula, whereby a set stimulus (S) produces a constant and predictable response (R). By controlling the sensory input, you gain control of the behavioural response. Feed a person with bellicose propaganda and he or she will be ready to engage in warlike behaviour. Smack a child every time it plays with its genitals, and it will develop a fear of sex and an anxiety about masturbation.

There is no doubt that this mechanism operates in man as well as in dogs and pigeons, the animals most frequently used in laboratory experiments, but with nowhere near the degree of inevitability that the Pavlovians suggested. In fact, in the case of man the really important ingredient in the S-R formula is the hyphen. This innocent-looking dash, which separates the stimulus from the response, represents the all-powerful human mind. This prevents us from acting in a never-ending sequence of knee-jerk reactions like a cockroach or a centipede.

How Lucky We Are

Thanks to the cortex of the human brain, we have freedom of choice and freedom of manoeuvre. We have the power to control, regulate and evaluate the sensory data we receive, and the freedom to determine the responses we make. Our senses may tell us to eat, because they are stimulated by the smell and sight of tempting food, but if we want to lose weight we can elect to overrule the signals and remain on a fasting regime. A stranger in a crowded lift may fondle our genitals, but we don't *have* to respond to their advances. If we prefer we can slap his face or scream 'Rape!'

Nevertheless we would be silly to dismiss the S-R formula completely, for it still has something vital to say about the regulation of human behaviour in general and sexual performance in particular. The earlier chapters of this book have highlighted the many and devious ways in which our brains can blight our erotic enjoyment. That is the hyphen in the behaviourist's equation; the all-powerful intervening variable. This, and the following five chapters, are devoted to the first part of the equation, the input of sensory stimulation which raises the level of excitation within the brain's sex centre.

Falling in Love with Love

The medieval courtiers attempted to have love without sex. Our great error today is that we try to have sex without love. To enjoy the full richness and vitality of our sexual relationships we must learn to make them more widely sensuous and less narrowly carnal. We must learn to communicate with our mates, by touch, words and sounds, so that we raise our mutual level of erotic preparedness. Other animals are so much better than we are at transmitting these amorous messages. The male camel, for example, is uniquely equipped with an inflatable soft palate, called a duala. When it is sexually excited, and in the mood for love, it makes its intentions known by inflating this balloon-like organ and puffing it out at the side of its mouth, rather like a large chunk of bubble gum.

Our sexual signalling is far more subtle. As we become sensually aroused our pupils dilate, our breathing quickens, the skin of the face, neck and shoulders becomes flushed, our hearts beat harder and faster and our voices become a trifle huskier. These changes are signs that our autonomic nervous systems are slowly preparing us for sex, rather than getting us ready to fill out our tax returns or take the dog for a walk.

These changes can be triggered by sensual stimulation, or equally well, and often more easily, by erotic thoughts. These days we tend to live in our heads, rather than in our bodies. We admire the cerebral and devalue the purely sensual. Compared with a blind person, we've lost our sense of touch. Unlike a tracker dog, or Indian guide, we've let slip our sense of smell. As a species we have become intellectually accomplished but sensually impoverished.

We have anaesthetised ourselves against the horror of our lives, closing the gates of perception so that we do not notice the terror and violence around us. We deaden our senses to the media reports of violence, murder, rape, poverty, starvation and death. Like the *mussulmen* of the concentration camps we function but do not feel. But in blocking out the pain we also shield ourselves from the pleasure, for the opposite of love is not hate, but apathy.

Given this anaesthesia of the heart, we are ill equipped for love. And to make matters worse, when we suffer sexual problems, we are frequently dosed with tranquillisers which make our problems worse. Instead of increasing our level of sensual arousal, these sedatives dampen the level of excitation of the limbic system. This was demonstrated by Dr Alan Riley, editor of the *British Journal of Sexual Medicine*, who took a small group of women and gave them either a dose of Valium or a dummy pill. Two hours later they were asked to stimulate themselves with a vibrator, and then report their level of sexual response on a scale ranging from one to five points. With a high dosage of Valium they were slow to climax and gave themselves a score of only one point. With the dummy pill their orgasms were quicker and much more intense, rating a score of three points.[1]

We need to use our senses to the full if we are to achieve our full sexual potential. As one husband put it: 'If sex is the fire in marriage, then sensuality is the fuel which keeps it burning.'

Time to Get Ready for Love

Sex has got to be quick for animals, for safety's sake. When they're locked in copulation they become a ready prey for predators. So they're forced to keep their loving brief, like the buck antelope who said to a doe as they galloped side by side across the savannah: 'Let's make love. It won't take long, did it?'

We are more fortunate; we have no similar need to hurry, unless we have a TV serial to watch or are anxious to get the business over before the children catch us on the job. Unfortunately we live in an age when we are no longer encouraged to linger over our pleasures. We have no time to smell the roses, or see eternity in a grain of sand. The three-minute culture allows us time to copulate, but not to cuddle, caress, or carry out a civilised courtship.

T.S. Eliot spoke of the gap 'between the desire and the spasm'. This is a gulf which many people try to bridge long before it's reached. We want to land on the shore of satisfaction before we've arrived at the launch pad called desire.

Many people read the *Kama Sutra of Vatsayana* for its description of coital postures: the mare's position, the twining position, the yawning position, the 'splitting of a bamboo' and 'the fixing of a nail'. But the *Kama Sutra* has far more to offer than this. It also contains some splendid advice on courtship. The man should sit beside his partner, it recommends, and stroke her hair, touch her dress and then circle his arm around her in a gentle embrace. 'They should then carry on an amusing conversation on various subjects,' Vatsayana suggests, 'and may also talk suggestively of things which would be considered as coarse, or not to be mentioned generally in society. They may then sing, either with or without gesticulations, and play on musical instruments, talk about the arts, and persuade each other to drink.' It is only after this long period of sensory stimulation, 'when the woman is overcome with love and desire', that the couple are judged to be ready for sexual congress. And what woman, when aroused in this patient and romantic fashion, would not be ready by that time to split the bamboo, fix the nail or do anything else her lover fancied?

We have lost the delicious, sensual art of pre-copulatory foreplay in our quest for quick results. Not so the majority of tribal peoples, who are generally gentler and far more considerate lovers than their 'civilised' counterparts. Bantu youngsters have to undergo an arduous initiation process before they are formally admitted into manhood. Immediately their rite of passage is over, they are given a three-week course in sexual technique by the tribal witch doctor. At the end of this period of instruction they have to pass a practical test of competence. They are visited at night by a mature, naked woman, who is heavily masked to conceal her identity. If the woman finds the boy to be a proficient, considerate lover he is allowed to become an elder of the tribe. If not – and if he is found to be thoughtless, clumsy, or too quick to reach an orgasm – he is confined to the initiation hut for further training.[2]

Young men, if they are members of the Xhosa tribe, have to pass a further test on their wedding night. This they spend, not with their brides, but with their mothers-in-law, who have a further chance to test their sexual prowess. This novel arrangement has one serious drawback. If the young man proves *too* good a lover, he sometimes elopes with his mother-in-law.

How many of our young men are equally proficient? Would it not be helpful if they too had to pass an amatory proficiency test – not necessarily with their mother-in-law – before they were given the freedom of the bedroom? This suggestion would certainly have met with the approval of Honoré de Balzac, who complained that to marry a girl to an inexperienced husband was liking giving a violin to an orang-utan.

It seems that tenderness is the one thing that women long for in a lover, and so rarely find. This was confirmed by a vast survey carried out on St Valentine's Day for the French radio station France-Inter. It showed that while French women liked their men to be attractive, sexy and faithful, the quality they looked for most was 'tenderness'. This disarming, masculine attribute was top of the list for 59 per cent of the women polled.[3] French men liked their lovers to be attentive and sweet, but not aggressively sexy. Two out of three were attracted to women who were seductive or coquettish, but only 9 per cent fancied blatant vamps.

Macho men sometimes feel uncomfortable showing *tendresse*: yet it is essential for a close, caring relationship. Marlene Dietrich was bisexual, but invariably preferred her lesbian lovers because they were normally far more tender than the men, and showed much greater awareness of *her* erotic needs. By contrast she found her male lovers – Maurice Chevalier, Michael Wilding, Yul Brynner, Jean Gabin and Ed Murrow – clumsy. The great exception was Frank Sinatra. 'He is the only really tender man I have ever known,' she claimed.

Western males rarely devote adequate time to the process of sensual arousal, and as a result are seldom adept lovers. Perhaps they never were, for an old French saying claims: '*Il n'y a pas de femmes insensibles; il n'y a que des maris maladroits.*' (There are no frigid women; only clumsy husbands.)

Three Little Words

The process of sexual arousal can start with a seductive look, a tender caress or a few romantic words. Even the most gauche teenager recognises that 'chatting up' is an essential part of the courtship process; yet it is an element which long-standing lovers often neglect. As one doctor, with a specialist interest in marital counselling, puts it: 'The most used and ill-used means of communication between the sexes, the voice, is usually a wasted asset. Something that should be soothing and endearing is often a nag or a whine, a grumble or rebuke.' How can a couple who have been engaged in a battle of words all evening expect to be in the mood for love when they go to bed?

The greatest aphrodisiacs are not ginseng, oysters and spanish fly, but tender loving words. In the same way the easiest way of quenching the flames of passion is not by sprinkling bromide in your partner's tea, but by dosing him or her with angry words. The world's great lovers came in all shapes, sizes and colours, but they had one thing in common: a mellifluous fluency of speech with which they could woo the birds from the trees.

Heloise was drawn to her lover Abelard by his voluptuous voice. Writing to him from her convent fastness she said: 'You possessed, indeed, two qualifications – a tone of voice and a grace in singing – which gave you the control over every female heart.' Centuries later the same might have been said of Richard Burton or Frank Sinatra, whose honeyed words and well-timbred voices set female hearts aquiver.

Men, too, are highly sensitive to a soft, seductive voice, which is why Ulysses' sailors were at the mercy of the Sirens, and Germans so easily seduced by the alluring voices of the Lorelei as they sat combing their hair perched high on a rock on the right bank of the Rhine.

The Trobriand islanders are well aware of the erotic appeal of the human voice. Their explanation for the relationship is simple. 'The throat is a long passage like the vagina, and the two attract each other . . . A man who has a beautiful voice will like women very much and they will like him.'[4]

Possibly women are more aroused by the romance of words than men. They seem to respond more readily to love poetry, smoochy ballads and romantic novels; while their mates go for the more blatant, visual appeal of the girlie magazines. The wise male makes use of this feminine predilection, and takes note of the words of Voltaire: 'The ear is the road to the heart.' Even if he can't sing with the fluency of Sinatra at least he can praise her charms. Maybe he leaves a love note under her pillow when he's away on business. One husband harnessed the enticing power of words by leaving his wife messages on their answerphone. 'When I get the message I know John's been thinking about me. It's flattering and I'm aroused,' she says. The key to this particular form of love magic is to evoke the power of words in ways which are romantic, natural and spontaneous.

Never Said a Mumblin' Word

The tender words of courtship undergo a transformation when they become the language of passion. The talk can then become decidedly earthy, which many people find extremely stimulating. This abandoned bawdiness serves to heighten the level of arousal. At this time words often give way to a more primitive form of communication. This lexicon of sighs, moans, squeals and grunts is known technically as eulalation. These pre-verbal utterances are to be encouraged, since they produce a further increase in sensory arousal.

In Roman times, sex was normally accompanied by these ecstatic utterances. This was so natural that soldiers and senators visiting a brothel were generally said to be 'snorting'. We're often too inhibited to give vent to these primitive cries of delight. Maybe we're worried that the neighbours might hear. (A hi-fi playing close to the party wall can help to drown the moans and muffle the tell-tale sounds of creaking bedsprings.)

A well-known women's magazine carried an article suggesting that men perform better if their wives moan while they are making love. One husband, feeling that he was being short-changed, read the article to his wife who agreed to give the idea a try that night. So when they were in bed, and getting amorous, she whispered in his ear: 'Shall I start to moan now?'

'Yes', he replied in a husky voice, 'start now.'

'Right,' she said. 'Why on earth did you come in this morning trailing mud all over the kitchen floor, and why are you still wearing those disgusting pants with the holes in them? I told you to throw them away weeks ago . . .'

Sexercise 7
The Sensuous Diary
Words have power to stimulate, whether they are spoken or written. One way to capture their erotic power is to maintain a sensuous diary in which you keep a detailed record of your love life. Write about your erotic dreams and fantasies. Describe your

first sexual encounter, the things which give you pleasure and the things which turn you off. Give a frank account of the features you love about your partner and your recollection of those special moments when you were together and the chemistry was divine. Then in future, when you want to get your sex hormones flowing, all you have to do is dip into your treasure house of erotic memories. You can do this on your own, but it's much better to share the reading with your partner for then you'll both be aroused together.

SUMMARY

- Whenever you want to raise your level of sexual arousal, take steps to bombard your sex centres with a concentrated stream of sensual messages. This can be done by following the techniques recommended in the *Kama Sutra*: exchange gentle touches, suggestive glances and words of endearment. These increase the level of erotic excitement and form an essential part of civilised courtship.
- Beware tranquillising drugs, which can lessen your anxieties and sexual inhibitions, but can also deaden your sexual responsiveness.
- As you reach a heightened state of sexual arousal, don't be afraid to give vent to ecstatic grunts and groans. These primitive cries of delight – known to the Romans as 'snorting' – will heighten your level of abandonment and arouse your partner. Words can be powerful sexual stimulants, but they are often not as potent as these non-verbal utterances.
- Keep an uncensored private record of your most memorable sexual encounters, and dip into it whenever you want to get your sex hormones flowing. Then, by awakening old memories, you'll produce the physiological changes which will make you ready and anxious for more of the same.

Eight

Sometimes When
We Touch

The skin is the largest organ in the human body, covering an area of approximately 17 square feet. It performs a wide variety of important functions – such as excretion, protection and temperature control – and is also a vital means of communication, especially during the early stages of sexual arousal.

'The most important of all the senses, in sexual matters, is touch,' said Van de Velde. This is confirmed by the women in the Hite survey, many of whom reported that physical intimacy was more important to them than genital sex. 'General body touching is more important to me than orgasm,' said one. 'It's the very physical closeness of sex that is the main pleasure,' claimed another.[1] This intimate bodily contact is equally important for men, as Shere Hite discovered when she questioned a wide cross-section of American men about their sexual preferences. 'Most of the men who answered gave physical closeness and overall bodily contact – full-length embracing – as the most important physical element of their liking for intercourse'.[2]

Tests show that gentle fondling slows the heart, reduces blood pressure and relaxes tense muscles.[3] It also stimulates the release of endorphins, which may explain why petting is such a pleasurable experience. We touch before we make love, because embracing, hugging, stroking, snuggling, nuzzling and fondling produce physiological changes which are the perfect prelude to sex. In the words of San Diego doctor Theresa Crenshaw: 'Spouses who enjoy frequent sensual touching feel better because medically they *are* better. And the stress-reducing effects of sensual touch can set the stage for fulfilling love-making.'

Man has the potential to be the most tactile of all animals. Having mastered the difficult art of standing on two feet, he has released his hands to act as manual antennae. Having shed our body hair, our skin has become more sensitive than ever to tactile stimulation. As a result of these two dramatic changes the Naked Ape is now ideally equipped for non-verbal communication. In practice, unfortunately, we have so often surrounded ourselves with touch taboos that it becomes socially unacceptable for us to get the stimulus we so desperately need. As a result, many people today are suffering from touch deprivation. This is the malady which the encounter group movement tried to remedy in the 1960s, with its group hug-ins, sensory awareness workshops and sessions of nude body massage. Outsiders might have scoffed at these bizarre antics, but they did represent a valid attempt to find a solution to a serious contemporary dilemma.

This was recognised by Desmond Morris who, on the final page of *Intimate Behaviour*, wrote: 'We laugh at educated adults who pay large sums to go and play childish games of touch and hug in scientific institutes, and we fail to see the signs. How much better it would be if we could accept the fact that tender loving is not a weakly thing, only for infants and young lovers; if we could release our feelings, and indulge ourselves in an occasional and magical return to intimacy.'[4]

We try to remedy our sexual problems by a process of thinking and talking when they are often more easily solved by *feeling*. If your sexual relations are unsatisfactory at present, try taking your minds out of the equation and giving your bodies a chance to become acquainted.

One psychoanalyst took this course of action and found it embarrassingly successful. He took part in a sexual expansion workshop which involved a series of tactile and sensual exercises, and at the end exclaimed: 'How can I go back to giving purely verbal therapy when I know that one touch is worth a thousand words?'[5]

Cuddle Up a Little Closer

Love has been described as the meeting of two minds and the contact of two skins. The meeting of the minds is generally easy to achieve, but problems can arise from our inability to establish intimate, flesh-to-flesh contact. That is the communication gap we need to bridge.

The more crowded societies become, the more rigidly we impose restrictions on close bodily contact. We like to maintain a 'no-go' area around our bodies; a private space into which others are forbidden to trespass. In most Western societies this 'personal distance' is about 4 to 12 feet. Any closer contact becomes a source of embarrassment unless it is an intimate encounter between lovers, between parents and children, or an approved intimacy between doctors and patients. (We enjoy being touched by hairdressers, masseurs and osteopaths, because this satisfies our tactile needs in a socially acceptable fashion.)

These barriers to physical intimacy are particularly strong in North

America and Britain. A team of sociologists visited eight different countries and counted the number of times people touched each other while they were talking together in cafés and restaurants. The tallies varied enormously. The most prolific touchers proved to be the inhabitants of San Juan, Puerto Rico, who scored 180 hand contacts during a two-hour spell of observation. At the other end of the scale were the icy folk of Gainesville, Florida, who made no more than two physical contacts during the entire two hour period of study. Finally came the Londoners who, true to their stand-offish reputation, made no contact at all.

The tendency to touch, or remain apart, is part of our cultural heritage. The Mediterranean races are brought up to enjoy close physical contact, whereas Britons and North Americans are schooled to keep their distance. This national variation was clearly shown when the scores for the various towns were added together, country by country. When the summaries were analysed it was found that the Greeks were the most prolific touchers, with a total contact score of over 500. The Spaniards came next with just over 400, followed by the French with only slightly less. The Germans, Canadians and English trailed well behind with scores of under 100. But the least tactile of all the nationals investigated were the North Americans, who registered a paltry 26 touches.[6]

Successful lovers need to get in touch, even if this means overthrowing social conventions and cultural taboos. This applies particularly to older people, who become less sensitive to touch as the years advance, as researchers at the Veterans' Administration Hospital, Long Beach, California, discovered. They took a sample of men aged between nineteen and fifty-eight, and asked them to signal when they first felt the tingling sensations of a small, vibrating instrument. The instrument was first tested on the right index finger and right big toe, and then on the penis, in both its erect and flaccid state.

The results showed that the sensitivity of the erect penis declines with age. So does that of the toe, and to a lesser extent that of the finger (possibly because the sensitivity of the fingers is maintained by repeated use). This decline in sensitivity explains why it takes longer to arouse the older man. His sexual engine still fires on all cylinders, it just takes a little longer to crank it into life. A considerate partner recognises this and is prepared to devote more time to petting and pre-copulatory foreplay when her spouse is older.

The Long Beach study revealed another interesting association between sexual performance and skin sensitivity. The men were asked to report how many times they had copulated during the previous month. The figures revealed a strong relationship between frequency of intercourse and penile sensitivity. This led the researchers to believe that the more sensitive our bodies are to sensory stimulation, the more likely we are to engage in frequent sex.[7] An alternative explanation is that more frequent sex helps to retain the sensitivity of the penis.

Although no similar investigation has been made into the sexual responsiveness of women, it is safe to assume that this too shows a slight decline with age.

All Of Me

For some while sexologists believed that certain areas of the body were particularly sensitive to erotic stimulation. They called these areas the 'erogenous zones'. Unfortunately, the experts couldn't agree which regions of the body deserved this enticing accolade. Most had no doubt that the lips, breasts, nipples, genital organs, earlobes, upper thighs, anal orifice and cleft of the buttocks were erogenous zones. But what of the other sensitive areas? Some included the eyelids and nape of the neck, others the hairline and the angle of the lower jaw. In the end virtually every area of the body became an erogenous zone, with the exception of the front of the shin and the point of the elbow. (No doubt at least one reader will write to tell me that they know of a shin or elbow fetishist who reaches an immediate climax when these unromantic spots are touched.)

If we accept that the erogenous zones are, by dictionary definition, 'areas of the body the stimulation of which gives rise to erotic or sexual sensations', then the entire surface area of the body is one vast erogenous zone. This was recognised by writer Joseph Heller, who once observed, 'The erogenous zones are everywhere, or nowhere.'

We need to make skin-to-skin contact, rather than launch a calculated assault on specific 'erogenous' areas in the hope that if we press the right buttons we will elicit the desired response. This seduction-by-numbers routine kills passion and stifles spontaneity. As one woman told me: 'He twiddled my nipples as if he was tuning a radio.' Hardly the way to induce sexual arousal for her – or for him. But there is an exceedingly close relationship between the erectile tissues of the female breasts and the genitalia. Stimulate the nipples, and the clitoris often becomes engorged. Fondle the clitoris, and the nipples respond by standing erect. This two-way relationship is so pronounced that Leonardo da Vinci's anatomical drawings show a communicating muscle running directly from breast to genitals. Marilyn Monroe confessed that she 'got goose bumps all over' when Clark Gable accidentally touched her breasts.

Teenagers seem particularly inclined to indulge in formula fondling. Wasting no time, they follow a set, *table d'hôte* menu. French kissing as apéritif; breast-groping and neck-biting as *hors-d'oeuvres*, then pants down and quickly on to the *pièce de résistance*. Their foreplay often follows a fast and furious routine – he's fast and she's furious.

Teenagers also appear to have a strange predilection for raising bruises on each other's necks. These love bites are probably worn as battle honours and do not necessarily indicate that the throat is a peculiarly erotogenic area. Besides, as Groucho Marx observed, 'Whoever called it necking was a poor judge of anatomy.'

Like the nipple, the earlobe is a particularly sensuous area. This could be because it is supplied by a branch of the vagus nerve, which plays a major role in many of the body's important vegetative functions, including the initiation of sexual arousal.

By twiddling the ear we increase the flow of gastric juice. (This was a trick used by aldermen of the City of London when they needed to stimulate their appetites to help them do justice to their vast civic banquets. This is why the branch of the vagus nerve which supplies the ear is called the Alderman's nerve.) Acupuncturists make use of this fact when treating overweight patients, sometimes with surprising results. Dr Leonard Sacks, of Los Angeles, inserted staples into the ears of patients wanting to lose weight and instructed them to twiddle them every time they felt the urge to eat. This produced the expected sensation of gastric fullness, but also made many of his patients feel decidedly sexy, possibly because the lobe-twiddling was activating their vagus nerve. One of the patients was a seventy-year-old man who had been married for thirty-five years and had been suffering from a lack of sexual desire. 'I knew his wife was a very passionate female who was frustrated by their sex life,' reported Dr Sacks. 'After the treatment began I met his wife and she threw her arms around me. She said her husband had become an ardent lover.'[8] And to think that after all those wasted years all it took to restore his libido was a gentle tickling of the ear!

Kisses Sweeter Than Wine

The lips are another obvious erogenous area. In many ways their moist, epithelial surface is analogous to the labia surrounding the entrance to the vagina. The Puritans, naturally, found it iniquitous for people to derive pleasure from mouth-to-mouth contact. John Bunyan, writing in *The Pilgrim's Progress*, said that he abhorred kissing, which he

71

described as an 'odious' practice. Others have been more kindly disposed, and have described kissing as the balm of love, the first and last of joys, the language of love, the seal of bliss, love's tribute and the nectar of Venus. Certainly the mingling of lips is an excellent means of promoting sexual arousal. It's also a splendid way for couples to get so close together that they cease to see each other's faults.

In the 1930s kissing techniques were taught as assiduously as copulatory skills are in today's sex guides. One slim textbook in my possession – *The Art of Kissing* – was published over fifty years ago and gives detailed instructions for performing a wide variety of kisses, ranging from the soul kiss to the vacuum kiss, eyelash kiss and nip kiss.[9] These procedures have one thing in common: they offer a delightful way of achieving mutual sensory stimulation.

Too many lovers feel that the erotic effectiveness of a kiss depends on its force, rather than its soft expressiveness. They want to demonstrate their passion by indulging in deep, penetrative kissing. They favour the French kiss, where the tongue probes deeply into the mouth, because it echoes the journey that they hope the penis will take at another, not too distant, time and place. (The French were less influenced by the Puritan movement than many other Western nations, and so gained a reputation for sexual 'naughtiness'. As a result they have always carried the responsibility for saucy things like French kissing, French letters and French knickers.)

Kissing, like fondling, should not be hurried if it is to give maximum pleasure and achieve maximum sexual arousal. This is emphasised by the author of *The Art of Kissing*, who advises his male readers to: 'Forget time . . . Forget everything but the kiss.' While your lips are locked together, think only of the pleasure you are giving and the joy you are receiving. 'Kiss her as though, at that moment, nothing else exists in the world. Kiss her as though your entire life is wrapped up into the period of the kiss. Kiss her as though there is nothing else you would rather be doing.' Nowadays we linger over our kissing only if we want to enter the *Guinness Book of Records*, like the Pennsylvanian couple who entered a 'Smoochathon' and kept up kissing for just over 130 hours.

The manual goes on to discuss whether it is better to kiss with the eyes open or firmly shut. The author finally opts for the wide-eyed approach, on the grounds that this titillates the senses of sight as well as of taste and touch. The matter is almost certainly of little consequence, although it does seem to arouse a certain amount of controversy. One man asked his friend: 'Does your wife close her eyes when she makes love to you?'

'Yes,' his companion replied. 'She can't bear to see me having a good time.'

Hold Me, Thrill Me, Kiss Me

The sex researchers argued about many areas of sexual physiology, but all agreed that fondling is a central feature of sexual arousal. Van de Velde advised his women readers to forget their everyday cares and worries and concentrate fully on the pleasurable sensations that came their way during love-making. They should, he said, make the 'conscious intention to enjoy all the stimuli received'. Masters and Johnson also advocated a total concentration on the voluptuous 'here and now', a process they referred to as 'sensate focusing'.

Sexual union does not have to be genital. You can get a lot of intimacy sucking each other's thumbs. Or you can copulate and remain a mile apart. With sex, it's quality that counts, not quantity. Better a tender handclasp with someone you love than a weekend of orgasms in fifty-seven different positions with someone you hope you'll never meet again.

The great tragedy of my youth was that teenage petting led to intense arousal but rarely to orgasm. The even greater tragedy of my mature years is that adult sex often leaps to mechanical copulation without passing through a preparatory period of gentle, sensual arousal.

Touching plays a part in the courtship of most animals. Many give it a prominence which we would do well to emulate. Norwegian lobsters copulate at night, the male approaching the female from the rear and gently stroking her with his feelers for up to twenty minutes. Then, when she is suitably aroused, he flips her on her back and instantly injects his seed. The amorous male octopus is another adept toucher. He spends many minutes exciting his mate with sinuous strokes of his tentacles before he ventures to impregnate her with his sperm.

With our naked flesh and highly developed hands, throbbing with tactile nerve endings, we are custom built for sensuous loving. Yet in our scamper to copulate we often deprive ourselves of this great delight.

How to Handle a Woman

Most women long to be caressed. They want wooing as well as screwing. Ann Landers, the famous American advice columnist, proved this when she quizzed her women readers. Many of the 90,000 respondents said that they would willingly sacrifice sex for loving embraces. It was tenderness they wanted from their husbands, not multiple orgasms. To confirm this more than seven out of ten replied 'yes' when asked: 'Would you be content to be held close and treated tenderly and forget about "the act"?'[10]

Many of the women interviewed by Shere Hite agreed that petting was often more enjoyable than intercourse. 'Touching is very important and meaningful, but doesn't happen often because men most generally have but one end in mind when they touch you,' said one. Another spoke of the frustration she felt when the male orgasm brought an abrupt end to intimacy. 'After sex it is very depressing for me if there is no hugging and kissing. I feel like a discarded shoe. But most men don't like to do this.'

Many men pet their dogs far more than they fondle their wives. But must a dog always be a man's best friend? Men risk losing their mates if they fail to respond to this deep-felt yearning for physical intimacy. This was one of the surprising findings of the Kinsey Report, which revealed that one-sixth of married women enjoy extra-marital relationships which offer petting but not sexual intercourse. Women, more so than men, are tactile beings. Most men have no difficulty achieving an orgasm through copulation, but for women this is far less certain. They climax more easily when they are manually stimulated, either by their partners or by self-masturbation. The Hite Report showed that less than 50 per cent of women climax regularly during intercourse. Most masturbated, however, and all but 5 per cent of these climaxed as a result, ten times the number who achieved an orgasm during intercourse.

Men who doubt the importance of cuddling and petting should read the Mills and Boon genre of romantic novels, in which heroines are constantly being cradled in their lover's arms and finally succumb to his tender caresses. They tremble to his touch – and, for once, not because his clumsy hands are frozen. These advances are effective, obviously, only if there is a close rapport between the couple. A woman will be roused if her lover fondles her breast, but will feel nothing but revulsion if a stranger gropes her in a lift. In the same way she can be brought to orgasm when her partner manipulates her genitals, but rarely when she is being examined by her gynaecologist.

Touches are generally imparted by hand, but can also be given by every other mobile part of the human anatomy – feet, cheek, eyelashes, hair and legs. Nuzzling with the nose can be highly exciting for some. The tongue is another highly tactile organ. Physiologists measure skin sensitivity by what is known as the two-point discrimination test. They see how far apart two stimuli have to be – say the pressure of two pencil points – before they are separately felt. In the case of the relatively insensitive skin in the middle of the back the pressure points have to be at least 2.5 inches apart for the separate impressions to be felt. On the forearms the distance is 1.5 inches; on the palm of the hand 0.25 and on the fingertip 0.1 inch. But the most sensitive part of the human body is the tip of the tongue, which can detect sensations which are only 0.025 inches apart. This delicate organ merits far wider use in quality love-making: probing earlobes, caressing eyelids, sucking fingers, licking armpits, fondling toes.

Body licking is an integral part of animal courtship and grooming. In most cases this includes oral stimulation of the genitalia. The anthropologist Dr Ashley Montagu made a particular study of this practice and concluded that: 'One of the elements in the genesis of the ability to love is "licking", or its equivalent in other forms of pleasurable stimulation.'[11] He reported that bitches, immediately after giving birth, spend 30 to 50 per cent of their time licking their puppies' bodies, particularly over their anogenital area. Failure to do so results in incomplete development of their offspring's genitourinary system and an increased mortality rate, unless some substitute is found for the maternal licking – such as stroking by the researcher's hand.

Other experiments have shown that licking helps to accelerate the development of the mammary glands in pregnant rats. Female rats normally spend a considerable time licking their bodies. If for any reason they are unable to do so when they are pregnant their breast growth is inhibited.[12]

Licking may be equally important for human mammals, and yet it is rarely practised freely except by certain primitive tribes who haven't yet been tainted by Western inhibitions and taboos. An anthropologist who visited the bushmen of the Kalahari Desert reported that they lavish affection on their babies. 'They are kissed on their faces, bellies, genitals; sung to, bounced, entertained, encouraged, even addressed at length in conversational tones long before they can understand words.'[13] By contrast, he said, the American child was 'deprived' of physical stimulation.

Put Your Arms Around Me, Honey

Even though their need for physical intimacy may be less than a woman's, men also long to be fondled, petted, kissed and hugged. 'Hugging is the most important,' reported one of Hite's sample of American men. 'Soft, mellow hugs alternating with some tight, meaningful squeezes are fantastic. I'd even rather do that with a woman I love than have intercourse.' Can it be mere coincidence that the average woman has a 28 inch waist, and the average length of a man's arm is also 28 inches?

Another said: 'Kissing, touching all over, rubbing up against the other person and licking. I prefer gentle, feathery touching on my breasts and abdomen, and the inside of my thighs. I find that my entire body is sensitive when I know that I am sharing that space with someone I care about a lot.'[14] Men often complain that they are always expected to be the active partner during love-making and for once would like to be on the receiving end.

By getting into touch, we deepen our relationship. In the days of Imperial Rome people made friends by giving an overall body massage to strangers they met in the public baths. The ritual usually ended with the application of a strigil to scrape off the sweat and accumulated body oils – hence the term 'scraping an acquaintance'.

A mutual body massage, using soothing herbal oils, is a splendid way of meeting the need for physical intimacy and achieving sexual arousal. It also helps to strengthen a love match for, as sex therapist Dagmar O'Connor writes: 'The truth is that when couples start touching one another, they almost immediately start liking each other better, and the more they like each other, the more they want to touch each other. It's a delicious cycle.'[15]

Sexercise 8
Sensuous Partner Massage

Giving your loved one a body massage is one of the finest ways of getting 'in touch'. This is perfectly safe, providing the massage is gentle and confined to the muscles of the shoulders, back and buttocks. The instructions are simple:

- Spread a large bath towel in the middle of a double bed.
- Strip off, and take it in turns to be either patient or therapist. The patient lies face downwards on the towel, with the masseur kneeling to the side.
- A small amount of body oil is then applied to the palm of the masseur's hand and gently transferred to his or her partner's body. (Use aromatic body oils if possible, but failing that baby oil or olive oil.)
- Begin massaging at the neck, working away from the spine, and applying firm, even pressure. Keep the hands relaxed so that

76

they mould themselves to your partner's body, and try through-out to maintain a steady rhythm and even pressure.

- Work your way slowly down the body from neck to buttocks, maintaining constant contact with your partner's skin. (If the movements are too staccato, with regular breaks in contact, the massage loses its sensuous, relaxing effect.)
- When you have worked from top to toe on one side of the body (which should take about five minutes), move to the opposite side of the bed and repeat the process, working again from the nape of the neck to the buttocks.
- Then change places with your partner, and do your best to convince yourself that with body massage it is more blessed to give than to receive, even though it may not seem as enjoyable.

Do this several times a week and you'll quickly improve your massage skills and also develop a greater intimacy with your partner. Pair bonding among primate animals is strengthened when they groom each other, or pick nits from each other's fur. Body massage has the same effect, and is a far better means of pair bonding than the usual nit-picking that goes on between human couples.

SUMMARY
- Try to establish close physical contact with your partner, through regular touching, hugging, fondling and kissing. Very often relation-ship problems which have defied mental analysis and debate can be solved by *feeling*.
- Skin sensitivity declines with age. As a result elderly lovers need to devote more time to the process of sensual excitation, rather than rush into copulation before their bodies are properly aroused.
- Sexual fondling should embrace the entire body and not just the nipples, breasts and genital organs, for when couples make love their entire bodies from head to toe form two inter-twined erogenous zones.

Nine

Sweet and Lovely

Women have been using scents to increase their allure for more than 3,000 years. In Egypt, during the reign of Queen Nefertiti, ladies bathed in scented toilet waters, sucked pastilles to sweeten their breath and anointed their bodies with perfumed creams created in the temple laboratories.

At about the same time, Jewish women scented their bodies by carrying linen bags filled with myrrh between their breasts, and perfumed their homes by burning frankincense and aromatic sandalwood. (The word perfume was derived from the Latin *per fumum* and originally related specifically to smells created by burning incense.)

The Song of Solomon, which must surely rank as one of the world's most powerfully erotic love poems, is redolent with sensuous smells. 'A bundle of myrrh is my beloved unto me; he shall lie all night betwixt my breasts . . . Thy lips, O my spouse, drop as the honeycomb; and the smell of thy garments is like the smell of Lebanon.'

Then, as their intimacy grows, she recounts: 'I rose up to open to my beloved; and my hands dripped with myrrh, and my fingers with sweet-smelling myrrh, upon the handles of the lock.'

The mere reading of these lines is exciting. How much more thrilling it must have been for the lovers themselves, as they spent the night sampling each other's honeyed breath, tasting lips perfumed like lilies wet with liquid fragrant myrrh, and inhaling the scent of cheeks perfumed as beds of herbs, spices and flowers. This makes modern love-making, with its hastily applied aftershave lotions and roll-on deodorants, seem frightfully clinical.

Our grandparents scrubbed with soap and water to prevent BO, and splashed themselves with eau de Cologne to deaden the smells of rotten food and overflowing drains. Otherwise they had little time for perfumery as an aid to loving. We have gone the other way. We now spend vast sums on perfumes, which we use as chemical bludgeons rather than sensuous calling cards. The advertisements for such products, with their soft-focus pictures of Oriental harems and palm-fringed South Sea islands, are sexually explicit. So too are the brand names under which the perfumes are marketed, which all carry a promise of

78

sexual delight: 'Passion', 'Intimate', 'Joy', 'Tabu' and 'My Sin'.

The approach is crude; the results uncertain. There is no doubt that artificial scents can have an aphrodisiac effect, but not if they are used to excess. With perfume 'less is more', as Mies van der Rohe said of the architectural adornment of buildings.

Indole, for instance, is the substance which in small doses gives the delicious scent to plants like tuberose, hyacinth, lily, jonquil, narcissus and night-flowering jasmine. It also perfumes certain Oriental foods, such as the durian. This luscious fruit, with its soft, creamy centre, is reputed to have aphrodisiac properties. In fact the people of South-East Asia have a saying: 'When the durians fall, the sarongs rise.' But indole, in heavy concentration, is obnoxious and can cause headaches and nausea. This is not surprising since it is one of the more disgusting stenches emanating from rotting animal flesh and human faeces. A *touch* of a perfume, like indole, is sexually exciting; too much is counter-seductive.

When scents are used as sex attractants it is as well to remember that they are volatile substances which release their perfume molecules when they are warm. For this reason a dab of Chanel No. 5 which is just discernible in a cold bedroom can be overpowering in the close confines of an overcrowded dance floor. Conversely, scent is more readily released when perfume is applied to the body's 'hot spots': the breasts, neck, earlobes and wrist pulse. (This was recognised 2,000 years ago by Appolonius, the Greek poet, who noted that 'perfumes are sweetest when the scent comes from the wrist'.)

Freud's friend Dr Wilhelm Fliess regarded the nose as the most important sex organ. This might have been true of the court of Queen Nefertiti, or of the lovers immortalised in the Song of Solomon, but it could hardly be said of the average man in America, Britain or Australia. They are often hard put to tell the difference between jasmine and Jeyes fluid. According to Madam Rocker, a Paris cosmetician, perfume 'is everything' to French men and women. But to the English male it is of little significance. 'English men can't have any real sense of smell, to put up with what English ladies usually wear,' she argues. Perfumiers recognise this deficiency, which is why when a man asked for help at the perfume counter of a large London store he was told: 'Here are a selection of perfumes for wives – and over here is the more expensive range.'

A Nose for Love

The human sense of smell is very poorly developed, compared with that of most other animals. A police tracker dog can pick up a scent from an odour trace which is a million times weaker than that detectable by the human nose. We may have difficulty telling whether a glass of tonic is laced with vodka or gin, but a shark can smell one part of blood diluted in 100 million parts of water. The acute sense of smell of animals enables them to avoid predators, track down food and find a mate.

The boll-worm caterpillar is a pest which causes extensive damage to cotton crops throughout southern California and Arizona before it matures into an adult moth. The female moth attracts a mate by exuding a chemical sex attractant, known by the trade name of Glossyplure HF. When sprayed over cotton fields this scent attracts male moths from far and wide. Many become so stimulated by the smell that they engage in indiscriminate sex orgies, trying to mate with sticks, stones and random pieces of vegetation. In the process they fail to find an effective mate, which in some areas has resulted in an eight-fold reduction in crop destruction.[1]

Cockroaches are also being lured to their death with a sex attractant, known as Peiplanone B, which has been isolated by researchers at Cornell University. This allure is so powerful that when a tissue carrying a trace of it was accidentally dropped beside a Jamaican swimming pool 'within minutes the area was black with tens of thousands of male cockroaches who had swarmed out of the sewer pipe'.[2]

Pigs spread their sexual allure by mouth. When a boar feels randy he slobbers at the mouth and breathes heavily in the direction of his chosen mate. If the sow is in a receptive mood, the whiff of his breath arouses her and encourages her to arch her back and offer herself for mounting. The male porcupine does things differently. When he wants to send a perfumed *billet-doux* to a potential partner he stands on his hind legs and sprays her with his urine.

Humans have similar ways of chemical communication, which are less appreciated and far less widely used.

Move in a Little Closer Baby

Though we may not be aware of it, the air around us teems with chemical messengers, known collectively as pheromones, from the

Greek *pherein* (to carry) and *horman* (to excite). These airborne molecules carry a wide range of information which has a profound influence on our behaviour and mood. With every breath we take these tiny particles are wafted to the top of our nasal cavities, where our olfactory receptor cells are housed. From here the information is relayed to one of the most primitive parts of the brain, which in the days when I was doing my medical studies was still called the rhinencephalon or 'nose brain'. (Now it is regarded as part of the limbic system.)

This olfactory pathway is active from the moment we are born. The earliest human love affair – between babies and their mothers – is dominated by smell. Experiments carried out at the University of California have shown that babies can distinguish the smell of their mothers from that of other women from the age of six weeks onwards. In many cases they will only begin sucking in response to their mother's smell.[3]

The California researchers proved that adults as well as babies possess the ability to detect individuals by their smell. They asked a group of male and female student volunteers to wear a T-shirt for a day and to wash themselves only with water. Each student was then given a selection of three of the used shirts. One was their own, another had been worn by a man and the third by a woman. They were then asked to pick out their own garment and decide whether the other two had been worn by a male or female. Their success rate in both tests was very high, suggesting that our smells may be as distinctive as our fingerprints and faces.

When we judge people, we do so not only on the basis of their appearance and behaviour, but also on account of their smell. For generations doctors have used their noses to diagnose disease. Phenylketonuria smells 'like stale, sweaty, locker-room towels'; typhoid fever like 'fresh-baked brown bread', while yellow fever gives off a scent 'reminiscent of a butcher's shop.'[4] To this can be added the account of a Welsh doctor, who claims that measles creates an odour like 'newly plucked feathers' and 'flu 'a smell like cleaning fluid'.[5]

Red Roses for a Blue Lady

As well as giving an indication of a person's health, smell was at one time considered to give a clue to their moral standards. Saints were believed to have the 'odour of sanctity', a flower-like scent variously described as lavender, lilies, violets, roses, myrrh or frankincense. St Francis was reported to have smelled like musk, St Lydwine of cinnamon and St Cajetan of orange blossom – 'because he was a virgin'. Sinners gave off a totally different odour. This was believed to be so distinctive that St Pachomius, having sniffed the cloak of a young girl, was immediately able to denounce her as a fornicator. (A cynical eighteenth-century French historian suggested that in order to develop his sense of smell to the point when he could recognise a woman of loose morals by the mere smell of her coat, 'it must have been necessary in the course of his ministry to come into very close contact with a great many of them'.[6])

Animals make use of pheromones, not only as sex attractants, but also to help them locate food, mark their territory, maintain their position in the pecking order and transmit danger signals. We may use them in similar ways. Certainly it's widely believed that animals can tell when we're afraid, and at least one expert suggests that passions were inflamed during the Nuremberg rallies when arms were raised in the Nazi salute and the air filled with pheromones released from the armpits of the highly excited crowd.

These ideas are speculative, but there is no doubt that smells have a profound effect of human sexual function. For instance, it is well established that women who are close friends, or live together, tend to have periods at roughly the same time. This 'menstrual synchronicity' is believed to be due to pheromone transfer. This was shown by experiments carried out by psychologist Michael Russell of San Francisco State University. He took samples of the underarm secretions of a colleague, named Genevieve, who didn't shave under her armpits and didn't use deodorants. He then spread her natural perfume – which he discreetly dubbed 'Essence of Genevieve' – on the lips of five female volunteers. He did this three times a week, and gradually, over a spell of four months, the menstrual cycles of the women began to converge. By the end of the test period four of the five women had synchronised to within a day of Genevieve's cycle, whereas a control group of six, who had had neat alcohol dabbed on their lips, showed no change whatsoever.[7]

This shows that pheromones, transmitted by one person, can affect the behaviour and sexual function of another. When people look at pornographic photographs they are aroused in ways which scientists can easily observe and measure. But these responses are noticeably greater if the pictures are impregnated with androsterol, one of the principal pheromones in human sweat. A similar experiment, carried out at the University of California, disclosed that people are drawn to objects sprayed with minute traces of armpit scent, even if the smell isn't consciously noticed. The test was carried out in public toilets equipped with rows of cubicles, and revealed that one toilet could be given a far greater appeal than the others simply by smearing its handle with a smidgin of armpit pheromones.[8]

The apocrine glands, which are located in the armpits and genital areas, produce secretions which are powerful sex attractants. Unfortunately, now that we have assumed the upright posture, we are not so well placed to appreciate their odour. In polite company we can't get down on all fours like dogs and sniff each other's genitals. But we can make better use of the 'Eau de Genevieve' wafting from our armpits. Because these glands are conveniently placed at nose height they are, according to one expert, 'superior in attractive power to the scent of the sexual organs or any other part of the body.'[9] But far from using this heaven-sent perfume to win friends and influence people, we spend a fortune trying to obliterate it with soap, showers, scrubbing, scented powders and deodorant sprays.

It's Magic

The non-Caucasian races, whom we openly patronise but secretly envy, are far wiser. They are as anxious to preserve their sexual potency as we are, but they are not tied down by sexual taboos and so are perfectly prepared to exploit to the full the aphrodisiac powers of their bodily secretions. The power of these is recognised by the Trobriand islanders, who claim that if love magic is to work it must enter through the nose.[10]

This theme recurs throughout tribal love practices, which often make use of potions containing semen or genital secretions.

Our reliance on sexual scents is poor compared with that of a Trobriand islander, and insignificant compared to that of the vast majority of animals. Smell is a sense we rarely use and which is unequally shared out among the human population. Most people can recognise about 4,000 distinct scents, but some can identify twice or three times that number. For some reason black people have a better sense of smell than people with fair skins. As this also applies to rabbits and dogs, it may be because of the increased pigmentation of their olfactory mucous membranes. This would also explain the more powerful noses of black-haired people compared with those of people with fairer hair.

The sexes also differ in their sense of smell. Masculine sweat contains a pheromone called androsterone. This smell is readily perceived by young women, especially during the middle of their menstrual cycles, when they are at their most fertile. They recognise it as a pleasant, musky smell. This explains why natural musk, from the Indian musk deer, has gained such a universal reputation as an aphrodisiac, and has become so popular as a perfume ingredient. Unfortunately, the scent is not so well perceived by men, more than half of whom do not notice it even if it is wafted directly under their nostrils.

Male pigs and wild boars also secrete androsterone in their sweat. Among a herd of pigs the release of androsterone stimulates mating behaviour, making the males more aggressive and the females more receptive. In humans its effect is somewhat different. Even when the scent is not consciously noted, it makes people happier and more friendly. For women it can also act as a powerful attractant. A series of tests has shown that women will unwittingly select waiting-room chairs, theatre seats and telephones booths which have been pre-sprayed with androsterone. Other experiments have revealed that portrait photographs are rated as more interesting and attractive when the viewers have been secretly aroused by a whiff of androsterone. It also appears to increase the sexual activity of men, causing men who are high secretors of the pheromone to have an above-average number of children and an increased risk of divorce.[11]

Another pheromone, known as isovaleric acid (IVA), is found in the genital secretions of women. This is sometimes referred to as 'copulin', since it is a major inducement to copulation in gorillas and other higher apes. In small doses IVA is pleasing; in large doses it becomes offensive. As its production is stimulated by the secretion of oestrogen, its scent is most powerful at the time of ovulation, when fertility is at its height. Conversely its production falls when women take the progesterone-only contraceptive pill.

I Like it, I Like it

For some while vets have been using spray cans of androsterone, known as Boarmate, to encourage sows to adopt a receptive, mating posture. Some pig farmers have used the scent themselves, in the hope that it will improve their own mating prospects. Several have gone into pubs with a dusting of Boarmate on their clothes and claim that it had a remarkable effect, arousing the amorous interests of barmaids and lady customers alike.

The sex shops quickly recognised the commercial potential of the substance, and started marketing Boarmate in handy-sized aerosol sprays under the trade name Aeolus 7. 'Attract women,' the advertisements proclaimed. 'The scientific way to help ensure success with ladies is to use Aeolus 7 – a male sex pheromone which has a scent that attracts females.' What the advertisements didn't divulge is that androsterone does not work in crowded rooms and is effective only in intimate encounters. This led one of the leading pheromone researchers to advise young men to try their luck with Boarmate rather than the much more expensive sex aid. 'This not only offers economy of size,' he wrote, 'but would enable any hopeful sprayer to screen larger groups of potential partners.'[12]

Recent studies also suggest that women are healthier when they come into regular close contact with male pheromones. This is the experience of Dr Winnifred Cutler, a specialist in behavioural endocrinology at the Howell Chemical Senses Center, Philadelphia, who has found that women who have heterosexual sex at least once a week are more likely to have normal menstrual cycles, fewer infertility problems and fewer menopausal troubles than women who are celibate or have sex at infrequent intervals. 'My dream is that manufactured male essence – in creams, sprays or perfumes – can dramatically alter the well-being of women,' said Dr Cutler. But one of her colleagues warned: 'Women don't get the effect working in offices or classrooms with men. It has to be intimate contact.'

In Bad Odour

When pheromones work, they do so best in minute concentrations, when they are often below the level of conscious perception. The moment bodily odours become overpowering they tend to have an anti-aphrodisiac effect. This fact may have been put to good use by primeval man, according to anthropologist Louis Leakey, who reckoned that early man owed his survival to his offensive smell, which made his tender flesh repulsive to potential predators.

The pheromone IVA, which scents the female genitalia, becomes overpowering if it is left so long that it undergoes bacterial decomposition. Then it smells like rancid butter or 'seriously unwashed goat' – the distinctive smell of sweaty feet or unwashed socks. The same applies to the pheromone trimethylamine (TMA), which is secreted by the apocrine glands of the armpit and perineal area. In small doses TMA is quite appealing, and is used to add flavour to such things as Bombay Duck, anchovy sauce and a wide variety of Asian fish sauces. But when TMA is broken down by the normal skin bacteria it smells of rotten fish. This is the distinctive odour which lingers around rotten teeth and causes bad breath.

Continental friends tell me that they are amazed that the bathrooms of so many first-class British hotels are not equipped with bidets. I tell them that if we ever feel the need for a sitz bath we normally do a handstand in the shower, but they don't seem to find the explanation convincing.

Certainly I would agree that a lack of personal hygiene can be a bar to intimate relationships. One couple were introduced by a computer dating service and kept up a courtship by post for months. They were reluctant to meet, because both had a guilty secret. He had smelly feet; she had bad breath. Eventually they got married and reluctantly they made their way to their bridal suite. It was then he told her that he had a secret and hoped she wouldn't mind if he spent a few minutes in the bathroom. Once there, he took off his socks and left them by the window to air, scrubbed his feet in the bidet and then smothered them with talc. Coming back into the bedroom he said: 'Darling, I'm ready.'

It was then her turn to confess. 'I'm embarrassed,' she said. 'I too have a secret and hope you won't mind if I go to the bathroom for a few minutes.' So off she went to clean her teeth, gargle with an antiseptic mouthwash and then apply a deodorant mouth spray. 'Now I'm ready,' she said as she gave him his first, lingering kiss. Then, thinking she ought now to take him into her confidence, she said: 'Darling, I have a confession to make.'

'Don't tell me,' he said, 'you've just eaten my socks.'

Unpleasant smells like this can kill romance. Henry IV of France suffered such appalling BO that his fiancée, Marie de Medici, nearly fainted on their first meeting. This would not have suited Casanova, who insisted that his lovers were 'always fragrant to my nostrils'. Napoleon, on the other hand, liked a much stronger body odour and whenever he had a chance to exchange the battlefield for the boudoir he would send Josephine a message: *'Ne te laves pas, je reviens.'* ('Don't wash, I'm coming home.')

The natural body odours which emanate from the apocrine glands in the armpits, crotch and perineal areas contain pheromones which stimulate desire. Since our sense of smell is poor, we have to make the most of these come-hither scents. This can be done by regular bathing with *unperfumed* soap, which helps to keep the pheromones fresh and free from bacterial decomposition. Deodorants, which can mask the delicate scent of pheromones like TMA and IVA, must also be avoided. But more important still, we must make sure that our attractant smells are in a position where they can work with maximum effectiveness.

Some women, when masturbating, excite themselves by fondling their genitals and then inhaling their own vaginal secretions. That's how close we need to get for our pheromones to work with optimum intensity. Anthropologist Leonard Williams has lived in close contact with a colony of South American woolly monkeys. Their body scent is strongest over their chest, and Williams notes that they spend a lot of time rubbing their noses in each other's chests. This ritual chest-nuzzling plays a vital role in their mating behaviour, and also in their mothering and social behaviour.[13]

Sexercise 9
The Oceanic Kiss

If we want to use pheromones to increase our level of sexual arousal we need to become as familiar as woolly monkeys. We must shelve our inhibitions and sniff our partners' armpits and genitalia. Male rhesus monkeys do this frequently, nuzzling and licking the vagina of females in the troop to find out whether or not they are on heat. And if an unreceptive female has her rump smeared with the genital secretions of a female on heat, she'll immediately find herself the focus of male attention. Even male monkeys held in isolation will become randy if they get a sniff of these pheromone-laden juices, and will find release by stepping up their rate of masturbation.

The human male who sniffs or licks his partner's juices, a practice euphemistically known as 'muff-diving', stands a good chance of being equally aroused. This has been demonstrated by researchers at St Thomas's Hospital, who found that women who rub their chests with their own vaginal secretions increase the frequency with which they and their mates have intercourse.[14]

Monkeys in captivity spread their scent around their cages to increase their mating prospects. We should be prepared to do something similar if we want to lead more exciting sex lives. Many country lads have employed the ruse of wearing a handkerchief under their armpits and then wafting it in front of the girl of their choice to draw her under their spell. A dab of genital secretions on the upper lip, hand or forehead can have the same effect. But remember, if you want to be aroused by your partner's smell, you must take a deep draught of their body odour, for only then will the scent reach the upper recesses of the nose where the olfactory nerve endings are housed.

SUMMARY

- In small doses artificial perfumes can increase sexual allure, especially when they are applied to the body's 'hot spots': the breasts, neck, earlobes and wrist pulse.
- Human perspiration contains chemical sex attractants, called pheromones, which can excite sexual desire. They work best at low levels of concentration, when their effect is subliminal rather than blatantly obvious. To harness the power of these aphrodisiac scents, take a smear of the secretions from your groin or armpit and dab it where it is likely to be most effective – on your chest, cheek or upper lip.
- Wash regularly to prevent the build-up of unpleasant body odours, but avoid deodorants and scented soaps which can nullify the effect of your sex attractant pheromones.

Ten

I Only Have Eyes for You

Sometimes the mood for love is stirred by a few words of endearment or a whiff of perfume, but more often than not it's triggered by visual cues. We're aroused by a glimpse of stocking, a suggestive smile, a seductive walk, or a tightly filled pair of jeans.

We find people sexy because of the way they look, not because they're kind to their grandmas or have an IQ of 180. We catch sight of them at the other side of a crowded room and even before we've been formally introduced we feel some measure of either attraction or revulsion. Men are turned on by breasts not brains. Shere Hite discovered this when she asked her sample of 7,000 American men: 'What things about women do you most admire?' The answers centred almost entirely on the female appearance: the erotic appeal of bare knees and boots competing with the lure of soft bellies, nipples, firm breasts, shapely thighs and a warm smile. And the things they found most likely to dampen their ardour were again largely visual – pendulous breasts, skin blemishes, dour looks, obesity, fat thighs and loose folds of skin.[1] Given this predominant male interest, it's not surprising that women spend a fortune on cosmetics, clothes and beauty treatments.

But women too are aroused by visual cues. Nancy Friday discovered this when she carried out her study of female fantasies and found that most of the women she interviewed admitted to looking surreptitiously at men's crotches and wondering how well they were endowed, whether or not they were circumcised and what sort of lovers they would make. One woman was such an inveterate crotch-gazer that her husband swore that she knew what side a man dressed before they'd even shaken hands.

Many women told Nancy Friday that they were particularly excited when they espied an erect penis, because this confirmed their sexuality and showed that they had the ability to arouse a man. This pleasure was well expressed by Mae West, who greeted a man saying: 'Is that a gun in your pocket, or are you just glad to see me?'

Women have always manipulated their looks to arouse male sexual interest, wearing figure-hugging sweaters, padded bras, plunging neck-lines, mini-skirts and slashed skirts to emphasise their breasts, cleavage, buttocks, thighs or nipped-in waist. Men have been far slower to exercise this power. Some pop singers have made sure that their vital statistics didn't go unnoticed by fixing a length of rubber hosing in their jea s; and a few men in recent years have gone to the lengths of having their scrotal sacs enlarged with silicone implants.

By consciously admiring the charms of the opposite sex, and empha-sising our own sexual characteristics, we can manipulate our mutual level of erotic arousal. If you want to be turned on, feast your eyes on whatever takes your fancy – balls, bottoms, breasts, bare flesh or bellies. If you prefer to feel less sexy, look instead at a knitting pattern or a do-it-yourself home maintenance manual. Do this and you'll find that like love, when sex is out of sight it's invariably also out of mind.

Hey, Look Me Over!

The eyes themselves have the power to charm, a fact we unwittingly acknowledge every time we use the word fascination, which comes from the Greek meaning 'to kill with the eyes'.

Eye contact plays a central role in the sex magic of many tribal races. When Bronislav Malinowski carried out his famous study of the sex life of the Trobriand islanders, he noted that they regarded the eyes as the seat of passion, desire and *magila kayta*, a word which might be translated as lust, but which literally means 'desire of copulation'. According to their understanding of sexual physiology the sex urge originated in the eyes, travelled up to the brain and was then transmitted down to the belly, arms, legs and penis. 'A man with his eyes closed will have no erection,' they firmly believed.[2]

The ability of the eyes to make the heart pound and the passions mount is well recognised in romantic fiction, where couples seem to spend a large part of their time exchanging knowing glances and come-hither looks. Usually the initial glances are short, for when we first meet we have to convey the message, 'I know you are there but I wouldn't dream of invading your privacy.' Later the looks get longer and more searching. At this point of arousal we are saying, 'I am intensely aware of your physical nearness and have every intention of invading your privacy if you give me half a chance.' At this stage, in the romantic novelettes, his eyes burn and hers melt.

Many women have made a fine art of this visual coquetry, using veils and fans to enhance their eye appeal. This skill was closely examined by the Spanish philosopher José Ortega y Gasset. He analysed a wide variety of different glances, but paid particular attention to the come-hither look given by women who want to attract a mate. This furtive look, which the French call *les yeux en coulisse*, is given through hooded lids to suggest that, while the sender is shy and playing somewhat hard to get, she is nevertheless showing definite interest.[3] This is the look which was cultivated by sex goddesses like Mae West and which is well displayed today by the Princess of Wales.

Not everyone has the aptitude to employ these highly articulate looks, but everyone can use their eyes to arouse their mates. The first, and most important, requirement is to find time to actually look at your mate. As one lady told me, 'My husband wouldn't notice if I had a sex change operation, or walked into the room dressed as an astronaut.'

People who are in love communicate with their eyes. This was demonstrated by Harvard psychologist Zick Rubin, who found that the amount of eye contacts couples made while sitting in a waiting-room was directly proportional to the closeness of their relationship. Most, without any training in non-verbal communication, can also use their eyes to transmit a range of sexually explicit messages. One doctor's wife said that her husband was overweight and going bald, 'yet he can still give me a certain look across a restaurant table and I want to get the bill and head for home'.[4]

The New Testament recognises the potency of these erotic glances and says that a man who looks at a woman with lust has 'committed adultery with her already in his heart'.

You Were Never Lovelier

The human body has powers to excite, especially when it is well proportioned and attractively clad. We often kid ourselves that, being cultured creatures, we choose our mates because of their intelligence, honesty, sincerity and warmth, rather than for their bodily appearance. But is this always true? In practice it seems that partners, women in particular, are often chosen for their looks rather than for their intelligence or social skills. This is particularly so when the choice is made by a young male. When male students at the University of California were asked to rate the attributes they found most important in a partner they chose physical attractiveness first, erotic ability second, and affectional ability third. Intelligence was of little importance, so much so that it failed to gain a mention in the top ten list of desirable feminine traits. For the women students the preferences were totally different. They looked first for a mate of high achievement, who showed leadership qualities and high earning potential.[5] This survey was carried out over twenty years ago, and one hopes that Californian undergraduates today might have a more enlightened approach to mate selection.

In making these choices both sexes were probably motivated by the same primitive urge. Without recognising it, they were seeking to perpetuate their genes. For men this is best done by choosing a healthy, sexually active, nubile mate. For women it is achieved by choosing a successful, powerful mate who is best able to protect and support her progeny.

But women *are* undoubtedly aroused by a man's physical appearance, although not, it seems, by the macho features emphasised in the body-building ads. This was revealed when *Village Voice*, the New York newspaper, asked a number of men and women to select the most erotic feature of a man's physique. The men were convinced that the features women most admired were powerful chests (21 per cent), muscular arms (18 per cent) and a large penis (15 per cent). In fact these power symbols were of little interest to the women, being selected by only 1, 0 and 2 per cent respectively of the women polled. What really turned them on were small, 'sexy' buttocks (39 per cent), a slim figure (15 per cent) and a flat stomach (11 per cent). These are all signs of physical fitness rather than macho power.[6]

'Foreplay begins with the eyes as well as the hands and body,' points out psychiatrist and human relations consultant Dr Leonard Zunin. We increase our sexual drive by feasting our eyes on our partner's body, and increase *their* interest by making them aware of how great they look. 'Make a random habit of watching your mate undress, telling him or her by your gaze, and verbally, how much you like his or her body,' advises Dr Zunin. 'People find such words of admiration not only sexy, but positive reinforcement to keep their bodies in good shape.'[7]

Unfortunately the reverse also applies. Fat, flabby bodies can do more to kill passion than bad breath and thermal underwear. Male impotence is sometimes akin to a flabby handshake, a way of saying, 'I'm not pleased to see you.' A man may be unable to get an erection with his plain, dumpy wife, but immediately aroused by the sight of the breasts and flashing, slim thighs of a go-go dancer. This was Henry VIII's problem when he first went to bed with his fourth wife, Anne of Cleves. According to court records, and the testimony of his doctor, he was rendered impotent by the shock of seeing her ugly body and 'the looseness of her flesh'.

To exist as fully functioning sexual beings we must master the art of visual foreplay. Our eyes must be trained both to transmit and receive arousal signals. Psychologists at the University of Illinois have identified the most obvious of these sexual cues. Without uttering a single word, a woman can excite a man's interest by looking into his eyes, subtly moving her body towards him, smiling, working her eyes over his body, widening her eyes, raising her eyebrows, and finally – the most obviously erotic gesture of all – by parting and slightly licking her lips.[8]

You're Sensational

Sexual excitement can also be brought about by the way we dress, and even more so by the way we undress. This is an art which has been practised throughout the ages. We wear clothes for practical reasons: for protection and warmth. But we also use them for personal adornment. Women throughout the ages have dressed to emphasise their sexual allure, wearing bustles to exaggerate their buttocks, padded bras to emphasise their breasts, tight corsetting to narrow their waists and high-heeled shoes to slim their calves.

The female breast has always been a focus of erotic attention as well as a milk-producing gland. This dual role is recognised in the Koran, which says: 'The breast of the woman nourishes the child, and delights the father.' Few men fail to respond to a plunging neckline. At one time the exposed cleavage was called 'the well of blessing', and became a receptacle for handkerchiefs, letters, flowers and purses. This ensured that it was a frequent focus of attention. Louis XVIII kept his snuff box in his mistress's decolletage, which gave him a legitimate reason to fondle her breasts from time to time.

Many other forms of feminine adornment have been developed to arouse amorous interest, ranging from fancy garters and suspender belts to split-crotch tights, navel jewels and nipple rings, which were all the rage in French brothels in the late nineteenth century. Well-chosen, feminine undies – soft, skimpy, see-through and smooth – are another potent source of masculine excitement. Their power to arouse is reckoned to be so strong that there has often been a taboo on the mere mention of a word like 'knickers'. Instead euphemisms have been introduced, like 'irrepressibles', a term which was widely used in the eighteenth century. Later alternatives are 'indescribables', 'inexpressibles', 'unutterables' and, the most popular euphemism of all, 'unmentionables', which originated in America and was introduced into Britain by Charles Dickens.

The More I See You

Men have also dressed to show off their masculine attributes. In the New Hebrides it is traditional for tribesmen to bind their penises with calico to form a large, erect bundle which they tuck into their belts and hold on proud display. In Southern Burma the Peguan tribesmen employed an even more blatant form of self-display. They tied gold and silver bells to their penises, to make sure their virile members weren't ignored.

Today's society does not encourage such unabashed displays of masculinity. We have taboos which make us reluctant to expose our naked bodies. This makes it difficult for us to strip off even in a nudist colony. Jack Douglas, Professor of Sociology at the University of California, noted these inhibitions when he shed his clothes and observed a random sample of sunbathers at a naturist beach in California. Even in this totally permissive setting, men found it difficult to offer the world a full-frontal view of their proudest possessions. 'This is a major reason why there are so many sunburned buttocks on the beach and so few sunburned genitalia,' reported Professor Douglas.[9]

Total exposure of the body in public is frowned upon, unless it is done within the confines of a nudist club, or is part of a high-spirited frolic like skinny dipping or streaking. Any man who went about dressed like a Peguan tribesmen would land up in court charged with indecent exposure. But nudity between consenting adults is different. In this setting it is not only permissible but also highly desirable. We all have within us an exhibitionist streak, which we generally keep under tight control. The men who expose themselves get a thrill when they see the effect they have on women. The same applies to women flashers, who are far more common than is often imagined. One well-endowed reader of *Forum* magazine confessed that she always sought opportunities to expose her breasts. In the mornings she would greet the milkman wearing a loose dressing-gown which exposed a lot of cleavage. 'My heart pounds with excitement as I feel his eyes riveted on my cleavage,' she wrote. 'When I bend over in front of him to pick up the milk, my dressing-gown opens further and my breasts swing out and for a couple of seconds are completely revealed to him.' On another occasion she posted a registered letter to herself, so she could give the postman a similar thrill when he called to deliver the package.[10]

These encounters are mutually arousing. This is clearly shown in the case of Celeste, one of the women interviewed by Nancy Friday. Celeste was making love to her husband in the sitting-room when there was an unexpected knock on the front door. She just had time to pull down her mini-skirt before their next-door neighbour arrived. He stayed for only a few minutes, but during that time he was obviously agitated. As Celeste recalls: 'I couldn't help noticing the way this guy kept fidgeting . . . and then I noticed this big bulge in the front of his trousers while he was talking to me.' It was only after he left that she realized that since she had discarded her panties and tights she had been giving him a full-frontal view throughout his entire visit. At first she was acutely embarrassed. 'Then the shock wore off and I was left with this odd feeling of excitement, which is still with me when I think about it.' That night she shared the experience with her husband with the result that they had a night of exceptionally passionate love-making. Thereafter, whenever she wanted to raise herself to a peak of erotic arousal, she imagined that she was exposing her genitalia to hordes of lovesick men.[11]

These erotic daydreams are neither peculiar nor perverse. They are a normal expression of exuberant female sexuality. Couples become aroused by the mutual exposure of their bodies. When we are emotionally free we want to dance together in the nude, sleep side by side in the buff, share a bubble bath, skinny dip together or – like Marie Stopes – lie naked on a hearth rug before an open fire.

Button Up Your Overcoat

Some Puritan sects went to great lengths to prevent any form of sensual arousal. When couples made love they had to do so at night, in complete silence and with no preliminary foreplay, kissing or fondling. To prevent visual stimulation, the wife was required to dress from neck to ankles in a purpose-built gown called a chemise cagoule, which had a convenient entry slit provided at waist level. Years later married couples were still reluctant to expose their bodies to each other and felt more comfortable if they retained at least their underclothes when they were intimate. (Kinsey found that a third of people born before 1900 kept their clothes on while making love.) To overcome these inhibitions, encounter group therapists introduced sessions in which participants took off their clothes and carefully scrutinised each other's genitals. Taken out of context, this 'goolie gaping' caused erotic arousal without sexual satisfaction. But performed by lovers, as an act of mutual admiration and sensual arousal, it can be most effective.

If you have hang-ups about exposing your body, make a point of walking about the bedroom in the nude. Hold a life class with your lover, and strip off and draw each other in the nude. (Even if this doesn't get your love juices flowing it's invariably good for a laugh, especially if you're not talented artists.) And if you feel a trifle uncomfortable about exposing your body, remind yourself of the words of Walt Whitman: 'Welcome is every organ and attribute of me . . . not an inch nor a particle of an inch is vile, and none shall be less familiar than the rest.'

It is unfortunate that the people who could be most helped by photo-erotica are the people least likely to tolerate its use. Yet we can all be aroused by sexually explicit photographs, films or stage displays of nudity.

At one time it was thought that women were not as aroused by pornography as men, but this is now disputed. Two psychologists showed a ten-minute erotic film to 31 men and 32 women and found that the sexes were equally aroused.[12] This is now an accepted medical technique for increasing sexual drive. In fact, Britain's Department of Health now has a permanent committee called the 'Advisory Panel on the Importation of Sexually Explicit Films for Health Purposes.'

This is a therapy which can easily be self-administered.

Sexercise 10
Picture Parade

If you want to increase your level of sexual arousal, build up a personal library of sexually explicit pictures and videos which you know will turn you on. Choose shots you can share with your partner. Remember it takes two to tango, so they've got to be films you both appreciate. If you fancy, take Polaroid shots of yourself in the nude, or play back video recordings of your favourite erotic scenes from TV films and plays.

Sharing auto-erotica has another valuable spin-off, which is not widely recognised. When you're aroused by a blue movie or a striptease dance your partner can suddenly become the most attractive creature on earth. This 'halo' effect was discovered by researchers at Kansas State University, who got a group of female undergraduates to rate the attractiveness of men depicted in a series of fully clothed photographs. They then took a separate group of 121 women and showed them a series of slides designed to produce erotic excitement, showing a range of sexually explicit activity from intercourse and fellatio to group sex. Afterwards they were shown the same set of male photographs, which they rated more attractive than the non-aroused control group had done. In particular they fancied the men's hips and crotches.[13] All of which suggests that when it comes to sexual arousal, a picture can be worth a thousand words.

SUMMARY
- 'Foreplay begins with the eyes, as well as the hands and body,' one leading psychiatrist explained. Look longingly at your partner's body and you'll increase your sexual urge. Flout *your* finer points and you'll soon get your partner equally aroused.
- Full-frontal exposure is one of the surest ways of producing sexual excitement. You and your lover will find your passions mounting if you dance together in the nude, share a bubble bath, skinny dip together or spend the evening lying naked before an open fire, like Marie Stopes.
- Keep a supply of auto-erotic videos and share them with your partner whenever the fancy takes you. This will make you randy, and also elicit the 'halo' effect, which will make you seem more attractive in each other's eyes.

Eleven

They're Playing Our Song

Nothing in life is totally static. Even a seemingly solid piece of rock throbs with the ceaseless movement of its component atoms. This constant, animated ebb and flow is seen more clearly in 'living' organisms, such as plants, trees, insects and fish.

Human beings themselves are never still. When we're healthy, we tingle with life and throb with enthusiasm. And if we show particular charisma we're often said to have 'vibrant' personalities. This pulsating energy lies at the very core of human existence.

We can be sexually aroused by touch, body odours and visually erotic images. We are also highly responsive to vibratory stimulation. Fish love to receive a pleasurable tickle. This was clearly demonstrated by Dr Campbell, of the Institute of Psychiatry in London. He rigged up equipment which enabled tropical fish to get an electrical tingle every time they crossed a beam of light placed across a remote corner of their aquarium. Once they had experienced this thrill the fish were avid for more and jostled and fought at the end of the tank to get a further dose of the electric fondling.

Newts and terrapins reacted in exactly the same way. So too did a caiman, a creature akin to a crocodile which is notoriously inactive, so much so that it often appears to be dead as it lies immobile in its tank. In Dr Campbell's aquarium it showed purposeful activity only when it was fed or offered an electrical tingle. Then it would burst into life, trundling backwards and forwards across the electrical beam at a rate of 200 times an hour, which according to Campbell 'is tremendous physical activity for a crocodile.'[1]

Sea animals in their natural habitat get their good vibes in other ways. Marine biologists have observed the courtship behaviour of humpback whales and noted that males set out to tickle the fancy of cows by swimming under their bellies and blowing a gentle stream of bubbles against their genitals. If the 'kiss' is well directed it acts as an arousing prelude to copulation. Bull whales are also excited by these love bubbles, a fact which scientists need to remember when they swim among schools of humpback whales to try to identify their sex. When they examine the soft underbellies of the males they have to take care to hold their breath, for they know that if they direct a jet of air bubbles against the male genital slits they risk driving the animals into a frenzy of sexual excitement.[2]

Other creatures employ a different technique to get their vibratory kicks. Most web-spinning spiders are short-sighted and so can't attract a mate by flaunting their beauty. To compensate for this they are highly sensitive to vibration, which also lets them know when insects are struggling to free themselves from their webs. Male spiders use this stimulus to woo the ladies of their choice. Since they are smaller and less powerful than their mates they take no chances with their courtship. Keeping at a safe distance, they behave like strolling minstrels, strumming away at the strands of her web. The female picks up the throbbing through her feet as she bounces gently up and down on her silken couch. If the vibes are good, she relaxes her guard and lets him take his pleasure.[3]

All Shook Up

Like spiders and humpback whales, we too are excited by vibratory stimuli. Both men and women can be sexually aroused by horse riding or by sitting astride a powerful, throbbing motorbike. Travelling in buses and trains can be another erotic turn-on, for women in particular. Van de Velde reported the case of one of his patients who was so sexually stimulated by train travel that she was driven to masturbate, a practice which at all other times she avoided and abhorred. (Van de Velde referred to her as an ipsatress, presumably because he couldn't bring himself to use the taboo word masturbator.)[4]

Other women get their genital tingles by using electric toothbrushes and, in at least one case, by sitting on a spin-drier. 'I personally find considerable satisfaction in perching astride my spin-drier when it is in motion and enjoy the ecstatic vibrations,' one housewife admits.[5]

The ancient Hindu love manuals had no access to spin-driers or electric toothbrushes, but recommended lovers to arouse each other with rapid, vibratory movements of their fingertips. The most effective sites for this manipulation were said to be the side of the breasts, the skin below the shoulder blades, the groove on either side of the spine and the part of the neck which lies directly beneath the ears.

The Japanese devised another way for women to enjoy a pulsatile thrill. They developed a device known as a *watama*. This was a hollow brass ball filled with small stones or grapeshot which was inserted into the vagina and held in place by a wad of paper. These 'love eggs' were said to be particularly popular with geisha girls and temple priestesses. Every time a woman wearing one of these gadgets moved her legs or rocked her pelvis, she sent secret shock waves through the walls of her vagina, which were quite capable of bringing her to orgasm.

For men the genital stimulation needs to be much stronger. Men respond to friction; women to gentle vibration. This is a difference that few men realise when they rub their partner's clitoris with all the finesse of a French polisher buffing up a tabletop. If men want to improve their amatory skills they should learn the techniques that women use when they masturbate. For a start, most women stimulate the area *around* the clitoris, rather than directly over the highly sensitive glans itself. Then they apply movements which are gentle, small in amplitude and above all rhythmical. 'I jiggle the skin over the whole area with a vibrating motion of my hand and arm,' confided one of Shere Hite's sample. Another replied: 'I make my whole body vibrate by tensing my arm and moving back and forth as fast as possible.' A third emphasised that as she approached a climax her movements remained small, but became more rapid, 'simulating a vibrator as closely as possible.'[6]

Good Vibrations

The ancient Hindu love manuals encouraged men to develop the art of sensual arousal. Few modern men are prepared to make the effort to acquire these erotic skills. Sex to them is an instinctive act which cannot be modified, learned or enhanced. Given this crass disinterest, they should not be too surprised to discover that today they are often being cuckolded in their own bedrooms by a mechanical vibrator – a lover with a much better track record and a considerably higher success rate. (In Russia these highly effective aids are called *palochkavyruchalochka* or 'magic wands'.)

Many women find it much easier to reach an orgasm with a vibrator than with a male partner. They tell me these pulsating dildos are cheaper, easier to manage, more faithful, simpler to switch on – and far less messy. This much I can understand. I can also sympathise with the women who find the devices objectional. 'It's like making love to a robot,' one patient told me.

The market is now flooded with vibrators of all shapes and sizes. All have their defects. The battery-operated models soon run flat; and the mains versions carry the risk of providing a totally unexpected sensation if they're not properly earthed. And for men, the mere sight of them produces waves of jealousy and angst. 'Why does she need me?' said one discarded husband. 'She has a better orgasm with her vibrator than she does with me. I only hope she doesn't use it when she's in the bath. If she does, when she comes, she'll go.' Another cynical Romeo consoled himself by saying that there are many other mechanical devices equally capable of increasing a woman's desire, chief of which are Bentley convertibles, ocean-going yachts and private Lear jets.

Shall We Dance?

Vibratory stimulation doesn't have to be applied directly to the body to be effective. Even from a distance it can cause sexual excitement. This explains the effectiveness of tribal sex dances, which bring about erotic arousal by a combination of nudity, music, dancing, singing and a throbbing drum beat. Sometimes the rhythm is created by pounding a stick into a hollow bowl of wood, an act with obvious Freudian symbolism. In West Africa young girls sometimes took part in sexual initiation rites, in which friction drums were placed between their thighs by older women, who pounded them vigorously to the accompaniment of suggestive gestures and innuendos.

In other cultures the sensual rhythm has been produced with a bone scraper or bull-roarer. The flute has also been widely used to create mood music to accompany sexual ceremonies such as circumcisions, menstruation rituals and fertility rites. Among the Cheyenne Indians it was customary for young men to use the flute as an instrument of seduction. Once again it is an easily recognisable phallic symbol. In fact, in many European countries the flute is a euphemism for penis. In this case, to differentiate it from the legitimate musical instrument, it is often described as the 'silent flute' or 'one-eyed flute'.

Many other instruments have been praised for their erotic powers, especially when they produce a sweet, vibrating sound, like the *oboe d'amore* and *clarinette d'amour*. Another love instrument was the nine-stringed cittern. The playing of this, according to one historian, was 'associated with immorality, a cittern-girl being synonymous with a woman of doubtful character.'[7]

Say it With Music

Music has charms to rouse the human breast. Our patriotism is stirred when we hear a military band. We rally to the call of a bugle and shed tears when we hear the soundtrack of a 'weepie' movie. Mothers crooned lullabies to soothe their babies to sleep and sailors sang sea shanties to strengthen their vigour. The sirens' song lured sailors to their destruction. Rats were led from the infested town of Hamelin by the Pied Piper, and king cobras were drawn from their baskets by the fluted call of snake charmers.

At one time lute players and troubadors were hired to create a loving atmosphere. Nowadays the seduction is carried out to a background of canned music. But if music *is* the food of love, isn't it time we had a feast? Why should the tribal races have a monopoly of the excitement and fun, with their abandoned dancing and passionate drumming? If you want to activate the sex centres in your brain, switch on some appropriate mood music and freak out. Shed your inhibitions, as if you were a South Sea islander dropping your modesty with your grass skirt. Feel the vibrations coursing through your body. Tap your feet, shake your head and let your pelvis rock to the beat of the music, making your movements as blatantly lascivious as you dare. Some music is tailor-made for this purpose, such as Ravel's *Bolero*, which the composer himself described as *'une danse lascive'*. Some while ago a sample of women were asked to name the music which was most likely to arouse them erotically. A high percentage found Ravel's *Bolero* 'the sexiest'.[8] This is not surprising, considering its pounding rhythm, which one psychiatrist likened to 'pelvic thrusts', plus its gradually developing climax, which Ravel himself called *'crescendo orchestral'*.

But choose your mood music with care. Remember, if it's going to have the desired effect, it has to excite your partner as well as yourself. You may be turned on by Tchaikovsky's ballet music from *Eugene Onegin*, but if he or she prefers heavy metal you're more likely to finish up in separate rooms than in each other's arms. This happened to a young man who was counselled by New York psychiatrist Renatus Hartogs. He was a music student and had made a fine art of melodious wooing. His usual technique was to invite a girl to his room and then set the romantic scene by playing some classical music designed to tug at the heart strings. His favourite seduction piece was *The Walk to the Paradise Garden*, the hauntingly sensual melody by Delius. But his companion one night was a very self-possessed young lady who wasn't moved by Delius at all and asked him to take off the 'goopy record'. She didn't want romance; she wanted plain, undiluted sex and to accompany it called for some action-packed music, like de Falla's *Ritual Fire Dance*. This 'undid the boy', reported Dr Hartogs. 'With its literal heaving and pounding this was pure fucking music.' The boy wanted to package his lust in a romantic wrapper; the girl wanted it raw. As a result of her sexual aggression, and the blatant eroticism of the music, the young man felt threatened and for once was unable to achieve an erection. 'So he and the girl just settled for a friendly beer,' an experience they could enjoy together whatever the background music.[9]

Waltz of my Heart

Dancing has often been described as a vertical expression of a horizontal desire. The erotic association is most clearly seen in tribal dancing which, with its parted legs, gyrating buttocks and forward thrusting pelvic movements, often provides an exact imitation of the sex act. These lascivious dances, which so shocked the early missionaries, were specifically designed to arouse sexual ardour.

There would be an outcry if these sexually explicit courtship rites were performed in Western dance halls and discos. The guardians of public morality would not tolerate the naked flesh, the pelvic thrusting or the lascivious chants. But although our social dances are very different in their appearance, are they so very different in their fundamental purpose? Even our bowdlerised social dancing is a powerful sexual attractant. At one time, before the advent of launderettes and computer dating, 50 per cent of people met their conjugal partners on the dance floor. It was on these occasions that they got the chance to hold relative strangers in an intimate embrace (it is no coincidence that the word tango means 'I touch').

Historians seem agreed that the new dances of the twentieth century, such as the charleston, jive, jitterbug and rock and roll, have done more to encourage sexual liberation than the combined writings of Kinsey, Hite and Masters and Johnson.

Poetry in Motion

Erotic dancing is a much neglected art form today, but is a skill which in the past was always highly prized by professional courtesans. The temple prostitutes of Bayaderes were trained as skilled companions and entertainers. From the age of seven or eight they spent ten hours a day learning singing and dancing and conversational skills. Once they had served their apprenticeship they knew how to delight their consorts, both mentally and physically. One Western observer described their dances as 'poetic pantomimes of love' and admitted that it was 'extremely difficult to escape their seduction'. Another gave a more

103

detailed description of their erotic posturing. 'At the commencement of the dance they throw aside, with their veils, the modesty of their sex . . . The sound of the flute, of the tambourine and cymbals, regulates their step . . . They are full of love and passion; they appear intoxicated; they are Bacchantes in delirium; then they seem to forget all restraint and give themselves up to the disorder of their senses.'[10]

The Japanese girls who served in the brothels of Yoshiwara, Tokyo's famous nightclub district, had a similar training. They were taken from the age of ten and taught to sing, dance and play a musical instrument. From thirteen onwards they were initiated into the mysteries of sex and, under the instruction of older women, they learned how to gyrate their bodies to excite their clients.

The young girls who were chosen to serve in the harems of Egypt and Turkey also learned the skills of erotic dancing. Their voluptuous belly rolls and hip thrusts were straightforward representations of the sex act. They were designed primarily to stimulate the male, but also had the effect of promoting and intensifying their own orgasms. Their dancing was energetic, which no doubt further stimulated the jaded palates of their masters by stimulating the release of attractant pheromones from their armpits and groins. It is said that Eastern potentates sometimes made their choice of nighttime companion by ordering the ladies of the harem to exercise vigorously. They then took a sample of their sweat-soaked undergarments, and chose the girl whose odour pleased them most.

No doubt the close proximity of perspiring bodies in discos and nightclubs helps to raise the general level of erotic arousal. The same was almost certainly true of New Orleans during the Jazz Age, when the brothel-owners encouraged their customers to whet their appetites by stomping with the ladies of the house.

Come Dance With Me

Dancing is valuable therapy for anyone with sex problems. Childless couples attending the London Hospital's Fertility Trust are now being encouraged to join classes where they take part in African fertility dances. In approximately one third of cases the inability to conceive has no apparent medical cause but appears to be linked with tension and stress. Dancing to the beat of African tom-toms helps because: 'You stop worrying about doing it on the "right day" in the "right position",' explains one of the hospital's advisers. 'You relearn sensuality.'[12] This may appear to be a bizarre foreign import, but Britons have been taking part in fertility rites for generations, either as morris dancing or maypole dancing.

Sexercise 11
The Merge

Anthropologists claim that you can tell the strength of pair bonding among birds by noting the synchrony of their movements when they take part in courtship displays. We too would strengthen our relationships if we found time for regular courtship dances. This was a regular habit of Wally and Lila DeWitt Wallace, co-founders of the *Reader's Digest* magazine. They rarely entertained, and whenever they dined alone made it a practice the moment the meal was over to dance together for fifteen minutes before they went to bed.

This is a custom worth following. Develop a courtship dance to whatever musical accompaniment you fancy. Don't confine yourself to recognised dance steps, or a rigid, choreographed sequence, but allow yourself the freedom to express your personal feelings and sensuality. Maybe you'll begin like a pair of courting birds, circling your partner and admiring his or her finer points. Then perhaps you'll start to flaunt your sexuality, shedding some of your clothes and showing off your finer points. If the feeling takes you try a spot of belly dancing, an art form officially known as *khaslimar* but often nicknamed 'navel manoeuvres'. Roll your belly, thrust your pelvis and do the shimmy with your open thighs. Endeavour to speak the language of love with your eyes and with every moving part of your body. Or try the exercise often given to novices learning the *danse du ventre*. Plant your feet firmly on the ground and with your hips try to describe the words: 'I love you'.

If you feel particularly daring, and are in good physical condition, sink to the ground and imitate the *khaslimar*'s voluptuous floor movements – the snake roll, the undulating floor glide and the shimmying back bend. Then, when the sex hormones are flowing, and the pheromones scenting the air, you'll probably find it time to stop your solo performance and begin a double act. Take your partner in your arms and give full rein to *all* your senses – especially sight, touch, smell and taste. Try to achieve a merger of bodies and a union of minds. This can be real love magic, a perfect antidote for reduced libido and sexual ennui.

SUMMARY

- Erotic arousal can be achieved by mechanical vibration. You can get this stimulus by using a purpose-built electrical vibrator, or through a variety of other activities which set the body's sensory nerves a-tingle, like horse riding, travelling on buses and trains, sitting on a spin-drier or moving gently backwards and forwards in a rocking chair.
- Sexual excitement can be induced by stimulating the body with rapid, vibratory movements of the fingertips. This is most effective – as the Hindu love manuals affirmed – when it is applied to the side of the breasts, the skin beneath the shoulder blades, the grooves at either side of the spine and the region of the neck just below the ears.

Twelve

Blaze Away

Dull folk make dull lovers. That sounds like a wild generalisation, but in fact the statement contains far more than a grain of truth. The sex centres in our brain need to be aroused before we develop an interest in sex. This happens more readily with passionate people than with those who live subdued, low-key lives.

We differ from our primate cousins in this respect. We need to be aroused before we can make love, but a chimpanzee requires no similar warm-up period. He can be idly scratching his ear one minute and copulating the next. Sexual foreplay is essentially a human need, a nicety not required by baboons, gorillas and orang-utans. For monkeys the entire sex act is over in a few seconds. For us it takes an average of about thirty minutes from the first quickening of desire to the peak of sexual satisfaction. Once we are excited, we generally find it easy to perform the sex act. Most of our problems are pre-copulatory. We have the necessary sexual apparatus and the required technology; what we so often lack is the interest and desire. This is where modern psychological research has come to our aid.

Walk on the Wild Side

Whatever we're doing, whether it's making love or adding up a column of figures, we perform best when we're suitably excited. This has been proved again and again in psychological laboratories around the world. Numerous experiments have been carried out in which subjects have been asked to perform a task – of memory or mental arithmetic – under varying degrees of artificially induced excitement. The results have been remarkably consistent. In every case performance has improved with mounting levels of arousal until an optimum level of nervous excitation has been reached. After that point function declines, possibly as a result of nervousness and tension. If the results are plotted on a graph, it is invariably found that performance follows an inverted U curve, which is sometimes called the Human Function Curve. These results are so consistent that they have been given the status of a law, known as The

Yerkes-Dodson Law after its two discoverers.

Many people today live in a state of permanent sub-arousal. They live banal, monotonous lives. They are perpetually tired, not because they are physically overworked, but because they are mentally under-stimulated, a form of exhaustion known as 'motivational fatigue'. This crippling ennui pervades the fabric of their lives. They are too world-weary to go out in the evening and have fun; too bored to tackle new challenges; too soporific to take up a new hobby; too tired to make love.

Some people try to overcome this malaise by gambling, driving fast cars, shoplifting or having extra-marital affairs. Others take up risk sports, like hang gliding, pot-holing and free-fall parachuting. Those who gain excitement in this way frequently enjoy a sudden blossoming of their sex lives. This is not surprising, for physiological arousal is not task specific. If you're about to leap from a plane, the level of stress hormones circulating in your body soars. This prepares you for the hazards of the parachute descent and also gives you the impetus to shout, laugh, turn cartwheels or make love.

Making Whoopee

When people are depressed, they experience a lowering of all their basic bodily functions, especially those which are controlled by the hypotha-lamus or 'old' brain, such as eating, sleeping, movement, mood, emotional expression and sex. Conversely, when people are in a manic state these activities are heightened. This is borne out by studies of manic depressive patients, 97 per cent of whom report that they feel euphoric during their regular periods of abnormal elation. During these upswings 70 per cent report feelings of heightened self-esteem, and 74 per cent an increase in sex drive.

Melancholics know that they can raise their mood by boosting their general level of physiological arousal. North African natives do this by indulging in wild voodoo dancing. Others achieve a similar effect by felling trees or playing badminton. Invariably these do-it-yourself cures for depression involve an increase in physical activity. When a group of students was asked what techniques they used to overcome temporary bouts of depression, most offered a remedy which involved some form of neurophysical excitation, such as brisk walking, watching a funny film, dancing or playing sports. These remedies are also useful cures for sexual lassitude.

Flash Bang Wallop

Branko Bokun, a Yugoslavian researcher who has made a special study of the physiological basis of erotic excitation, believes that fear is an important source of sexual arousal. Many primates get an erection when they are frightened or when they are taken into captivity. Stress can produce a similar response in humans. This is especially apparent during times of national conflict for, as Bokun observes: 'During revolutions and wars, when insecurity rules, sexual activity noticeably increases.'[1]

Anything which excites us makes us feel more sexy. The Romans got their kicks watching gladiator fights and Christians battling with lions. On these occasions their heightened sexual needs were met by prostitutes, who always touted their trade at Roman amphitheatres, just as camp followers throughout the ages have attached themselves to armies so they can satisfy the roused passions of the front-line troops.

These are examples of arousal overspill. In my youth teenagers liked to play party games which incorporated a risk element. Murder in the dark was popular because the excitement of the chase, the suspense, and the darkness produced a state of increased sexual arousal. This overcame teenage inhibitions and increased the chances of a cuddle in the cupboard or a grope in the garage.

When there wasn't a party, the same effect could be had by taking a back seat at a horror movie, or visiting a fairground and having a ride on the dodgems or big dipper. Courting couples have always preferred films with lashings of danger, suspense and violence, because they get them in the mood for love. One old lady, who was asked by a pollster if she thought there was too much sex and violence in the cinema, replied: 'I always sit in the stalls, so I don't see what the rest of the audience are doing.'

The Things We Do for Love

Many other races have devised similar thrills and spills to stimulate their urge to merge. The Peruvians had a licentious festival in December which lasted six days and nights and culminated in a catch-as-catch-can race. All the competitors stripped off their clothes and at a given signal raced towards a distant hill. Not many crossed the finishing line, for the rule was that whenever a man overtook a woman he earned the reward of laying her on the spot. In central Australia and New Zealand excitement was produced by swinging a bull-roarer. This sacred instrument made an awesome noise and was strictly reserved for masculine use during certain secret tribal rites. So strong was this taboo that the Arunta tribeswomen of Central Australia believed that they would die if they handled, or even *saw* a bull-roarer. Just its haunting sound was enough to chill their blood. Their menfolk took advantage of this, knowing that when a woman was frightened by the bull-roarer 'her internal organs shook with eagerness'.

Fear does exactly the same for Western lovers, as psychiatrist William Sargent reports in his autobiography. He recounts the story of a laboratory assistant from Duke Hospital who discovered that he could soften the resistance of his girlfriends by taking them to one of the snake-handling ceremonies held at a revivalist church in North Carolina. During these meetings people are raised to a pitch of tension and fear, which makes them susceptible to the preacher's message and equally open to sexual seduction. Dr Sargent, an international authority on trance states and brain-washing, reported that the young technician, 'found that when girls had reached the climactic stage of suggestibility and collapse they were no less amenable to his sexual suggestions than to Pastor Bunn's message of redemption. The young man would follow them out and easily draw them into sexual abandon. But he could not understand why, if he rang up one of his conquests a few days later to arrange another meeting, she would say indignantly: "I am not that kind of girl." '[2] But of course she *was* that sort of girl, and would perform in exactly the same way again if she had been given the right emotional conditioning. When we are suitably aroused – by watching horror films or handling poisonous snakes – we can all be surprised by our latent sexual appetites.

Friendly Persuasion

Psychologists do not place much faith in this kind of anecdoctal evidence. They prefer to put their trust in behavioural phenomena which can be observed in the laboratory or studied during field trials. Folk theories *may* be true, but they need scientific confirmation. So the researchers looked for ways of making an objective investigation of the link between fear and sexual arousal. A start was made in 1975, when two psychologists from the University of British Columbia, Vancouver carried out an ingenious stress test. The experiment made use of two bridges thrown across the fast-running Capilano River. The first was a rickety affair, with only low hand rails to protect users from a 230 foot drop into the water below. Crossing it was a hair-raising experience. The other bridge was far safer, solidly made and only ten feet above the river. In the course of the experiment men crossing each bridge were met by female interviewers who sought their help in filling in a questionnaire which was part of a 'psychology project'. The quiz included writing a short story based on an illustration of a young woman hiding her face with her hand. The interviewers then gave their name and telephone number and suggested that they would be prepared to explain the project in greater detail at a later time if this was needed.

Once the forms were completed they were used to assess the sexual arousal of the men by evaluating the amount of sexual imagery they used in their short stories. Scores ranged from zero for a total absence of sexual references to three for behaviour like kissing and five for sexual intercourse. The results showed that when men met a woman interviewer on the dangerous bridge their arousal scores were 76 per cent higher than when the encounter took place on the safe bridge. Also, whereas 50 per cent of the nervously excited men phoned their female interviewers later, this was an opportunity taken up by only 12 per cent of the men who made the safer crossing.[3] These results support the popular belief that fear, providing it is not excessive and paralysing, produces an increase in sexual arousal and interest.

The same is true when the fears are imaginary rather than real. This was shown by three researchers from Brown University, one of whom was the chief psychologist of the sexual performance laboratory at the Providence Veterans Administration Medical Centre, Rhode Island. In the first part of this experiment, woman volunteers were shown three two-minute film clips. The first was a frightening sequence showing a fatal car crash, complete with a blood-curdling soundtrack of the victim's death cries. The next was a relaxing travelogue and the third a pornographic scene of a nude couple indulging in sexually explicit foreplay. While the women watched the films their level of sexual arousal was measured by means of a plethysmograph, which measured the blood flow through their vaginas. As was to be expected they became aroused when they watched the blue movie, but their response was greater still when they watched it immediately after seeing the frightening film. Then their sexual excitement was also more rapidly obtained than when they were first exposed to the tranquillising travelogue. The same results were obtained when the experiment was repeated with a group of men, whose level of excitement was measured with a penile strain gauge. As a result the researchers suggested that 'there may be a future for anxiety in treating sexually dysfunctional people'.[4]

111

Beat Me Daddy, Eight to the Bar

Others get their excitement by either inflicting or receiving pain. The *Kama Sutra* devotes several chapters to this subject, giving detailed instructions on how to cause sexual arousal by scratching, biting and slapping. Love bites, slapped bottoms and pinched thighs can be exciting, providing they are exchanged by consenting adults as love play, rather than as acts of sadistic domination. Working-class women in the east end of London liked a bit of rough, and to encourage their mates would frequently say: 'If yer loves us, chuck us abaht.'

Nowadays the buttock-slapping, which would once have been done with the bare hand, is quite often done with SM whips and canes bought from sex boutiques. (*Playboy* magazine once offered instructions for making a spanking paddle, drilled with 'tiny air holes in the surface of the paddle to decrease air resistance'.) There is no doubt that pain *can* be used as a harmless way of producing sexual arousal. It is also clear that the obsessive *need* for sadistic or masochistic stimulation as a prelude to sex is among the commonest sexual perversions of our age. Often the dividing line between the normal and the pathological is ill defined and can be drawn only by the individuals involved.

Sexercise 12
Adventure Programme

Sexual apathy is often linked with boredom and a generally low level of physiological arousal. This can be overcome by injecting life with more excitement, thrills and spills. If this is your problem, set yourself an adventure programme designed to make your life more thrilling. Live dangerously. Break old habit patterns. Make new friends. Accept new challenges. Take up a competitive sport. Change your job. Climb a mountain. Go on a back-packing holiday. Learn scuba diving. Sleep rough. Take a night hike through unfamiliar countryside. Challenge your fears. If you're claustrophobic travel in a lift. If you suffer from haemotophobia enrol as a blood donor. Set yourself a definite programme of activities which you know will enliven your life, and you will find that your sex life will also be invigorated.

SUMMARY
- Sexual behaviour, like most other human activities, follows the Yerkes-Dodson Law, which means that we perform best when we're

in a state of optimum physiological arousal. Hype yourself up by leading a more vigorous, exciting life and you'll revitalise your sex life.

- Fear is a little recognised, but important, source of erotic arousal. So if you're suffering from the sexual blahs, you can give your libido a quick boost by taking a risk: gambling, watching a horror movie, going rock-climbing, parachute-jumping, or anything else which takes your fancy and will whip your body into action.

Thirteen

Ready, Willing and Able

The link between stress and sexual arousal is not quite as simple as the last chapter suggested. Most people feel more raunchy when they're pleasantly excited. That much is certain. But the sex act itself is also relaxing, which means that it's sometimes used as a means of release from intolerable tension. I have known concert pianists, actors and pop singers who copulate when other entertainers might pop tranquillisers or take a sauna bath, since they find this the quickest and most effective way of relaxing after a stage show. They become excited by their public performance, and calm themselves down as soon as possible afterwards by giving a private performance with anyone who happens to be around – co-stars, groupies or stage-door Johnnies.

Janis Joplin was one of the many pop stars who craved sex, largely because of its sedative powers. For her, says her biographer, 'sex was a palliative, an escape from tension that could not be endured'.[1]

The Australian Aborigines used the same recipe whenever the weather made them nervy or on edge. Most of us feel a trifle tense before a storm or when a hot, dry wind is blowing, such as the *föhn*, *mistral* or *khamsin*. Faced with these conditions most of us do no more than become a trifle more brusque and testy. Not so the Aborigines, who took steps to ease their tension. Before a thunderstorm, and during the course of the *aurora Australis*, they let off steam by indulging in promiscuous sex. This gave vent to their pent-up emotions and also, they believed, helped to ease the turmoil and stress in the great 'up there'.[2]

One of my patients, a leading Australian businessman, resorted to this remedy during his trips to Europe. He found that sex was the only thing that helped him unwind and get some sleep when he was under stress. So he kept an address book in his briefcase filled with the names of European girlfriends and prostitutes. After a day of high-pressure wheeling and dealing he would return to his hotel and have a meal and a few stiff drinks. If this did not ease his tensions in a few hours, he picked up the phone and made a rendezvous with one of the playmates on his private list. A few minutes in her bed, and he was ready for his. He found this the perfect sedative – not cheap and certainly not without its

114

occasional side-effects – but invariably relaxing and pleasurable.

Mental excitement is an effective way of increasing sexual arousal; an increase which is immediately lowered when the sex act itself is performed. But what if the arousal is *too* great, and a pleasurable frisson of fear becomes an uncomfortable burden of angst?

Take it Easy

This is a problem which sex therapists constantly encounter. 'Fear plays havoc with the sex life of tens of thousands of people,' reports Dr Eustace Chesser.[3] This experience is confirmed by Dr Helen Kaplan, who writes: 'There is no sexual stimulant so powerful, even love, that it cannot be inhibited by fear.'[4]

This is no paradox. Stress can act as either a stimulant or an inhibitor of sexual desire. It all depends on our place on the Human Function Curve. If we are on the *ascending* arm of the curve, and therefore below our optimum level of physiological arousal, we need a little extra excitement to perform at our best. If we are on the *descending* arm of the curve, we are past our sexual peak and need rest and relaxation rather than further stimulation. It's all a question of balance. A little of what we fancy does us good; too much can be debilitating. Or as the old adage puts it: 'Too much spoils, too little does not satisfy.'

Exactly the same applies to the induction of pain during foreplay. A little playful slap and tickle can be a turn-on, whereas the heavy use of a cat-o'-nine-tails is likely to be counterproductive (unless your partner is a masochist).

Marie Stopes, in the later editions of her book *Enduring Passion*, noted that soldiers involved in prolonged trench warfare during the First World War frequently became impotent. Under these highly stressful circumstances they had been driven to the very lowest limit of their personal Function Curve. The same happened during the Second World War, to military leaders as well as rank-and-file soldiers. Dr Theodor Morell, personal physician to Adolf Hitler, kept detailed diaries in which he recorded that the Führer, as the fortunes of war turned against him, suffered a profound loss of libido. Prior to this he had led a fairly normal sex life, fathering at least one illegitimate child and having regular intercourse with his mistress Eva Braun. Then, as the strain of the conflict mounted, his sex drive dwindled, a disability which wasn't cured by regular injections of male sex hormones.

Recent tests show that when men are under stress they suffer a drop in testosterone output. American soldiers going through officer training school show a significant fall in blood testosterone levels during the 'early, stressful part of the course', compared with the levels recorded in the later, more relaxed stages of the training.[5] Even exposure to aircraft noise can lead to a fall in testosterone output.[6]

In times of stress personal survival becomes far more important than the perpetuation of the species. Even the randiest of animals, rabbits and goats, lose their sex drive when they are threatened. When the hounds are in full pursuit of a fox, it doesn't take time off to copulate. He runs pell-mell for cover, knowing full well that there will be plenty of time for lupine loving when the chase is over. So it is with us. When we are overstressed we conserve energy by losing interest in non-essential activities, like going to the theatre, meeting friends and having sex. We also jettison our sense of humour, a symptom often linked with erotopenia. As one marital therapist told me: 'If a person can't have fun out of bed, they're unlikely to have fun in bed.'

Many workaholics today are caught up in this vicious circle. Under the pressure of their work they become tired and tense. This leads to a steady decline in their health and physical performance. To compensate for this deterioration they have to work harder to maintain their place on the economic treadmill. This leads to further exhaustion and yet more stress. Like soldiers, their libido is drained by combat fatigue.

Sleepy Time Gal

All living organisms have the ability to acquire and store energy. They also have the freedom to decide how that vast pool of energy should be spent. A lot of it goes on essential activities, like gathering food, keeping the body warm, fighting off predators and maintaining the body's internal metabolism. But once those maintenance chores are done, there should still be a lot of disposable energy left. Do we expend it on gardening, repairing the garage roof, working longer hours at work, moonlighting, running a bazaar for the Parent Teachers' Association – or making love? The choice is ours. We have the freedom to decide how we spend our disposable income, and, equally, we have the autonomy to determine how we spend our surplus time and energy. The way we allot these precious resources gives a very clear indication of our scale of priorities. If we're sports fanatics, most of our love games may be played on the tennis court rather than in bed. If we're house-proud mothers, we'll possibly spend more energy keeping our homes spick and span than in keeping our intimate relationships fresh. If we make these choices, we cannot complain if at the fag end of the day we feel too tired for love.

Women who stay at home lead lifestyles which are often every bit as stressful as a business executive's. Dr Marion Hilliard spent her life counselling women with health problems, and was for many years head of Obstetrics and Gynaecology at the Women's College Hospital, Toronto. She had no doubt that tiredness was the root cause of many women's difficulties. 'What detracts from the happy bedroom?' she wrote. 'The first and most important thing is fatigue. No doubt about it, a happy married life takes energy!'

Delving into her case records Dr Hilliard had no difficulty in producing evidence to support her belief. A young woman came to her in tears after a disastrous wedding night. 'Last night wasn't anything like I thought it would be,' she sobbed. 'It was my fault . . . I couldn't seem to *feel* much like making love. I just wanted to go to sleep.' The poor bride was so exhausted by the pre-nuptial preparations and excitement that she had no reserves of energy left for her big night. The remedy was simple. Two days' complete rest and she was once again an enthusiastic lover.[7]

Make it Easy on Yourself

Rest is a remedy which deserves much wider medical use. One East European businessman took it with great effect. He had been burning the candle in the middle as well as at both ends, and was finding that as a result his bedroom and boardroom performances were suffering. So he told his mistress he was going to see his wife, and his wife that he was working late at the office, and then went to a friend's home for a good night's sleep. The next day his batteries were recharged and he was once more his usual, ebullient self.

Sexual intercourse is an energetic occupation, whether it's a vigorous romp in the hay or a refined coupling in the missionary position. Metabolic studies show that on average it uses up about 200 calories, which makes it as demanding as half an hour's jogging. This makes it a practical way of keeping slim. (When film star Ursula Andress was asked how she kept her sylph-like shape, she replied: 'Loving keeps me slim.') Sex is flattering for your figure and good for your temper, but it does make physical demands. If at the end of the day you're too exhausted to run round the park, you're almost certainly too tired to make love. But why does the loving always have to be left until the fag end of the day? If you have the opportunity, why not a little nooky first thing in the morning, or during the lunch break?

A survey of Poles aged 18 to 65, showed that their most enjoyable time for love-making was between 11 a.m. and 12 noon.[8] So why not an erotic frolic with the morning coffee, instead of the usual digestive biscuits? Why leave the good things of life until the one time of the day when you may be too tired to enjoy them?

Our interest in sex knows no limitations of time and place. Introverts are generally more easily aroused in the morning and extroverts at night, but only 1 per cent of adult males, and 5 per cent of women, claim that they are sexually aroused only at night, according to a large survey by psychologist Hans Eysenck.[9] So why all those wasted daylight hours when we could be giving some of our most sparkling performances?

Time on My Hands

Workaholics, even if they're not too tired for sex, are generally too frantically busy to give it space in their crowded schedules. Each one of us has the same allotment of twenty-four hours a day. Our success in achieving our goals – whether of happiness, health, wealth or sexual fulfilment – is largely determined by the way we choose to spend these fleeting moments.

We often envy the sex life of tribespeople, with its elaborate courtship displays, love magic and uninhibited fertility dances. We attribute their exuberant eroticism to their spontaneity and freedom from inhibitions. This undoubtedly plays its part, but so too does their leisurely lifestyle. Among the hunter-gatherer tribes the male works an average of only two hours a day. This leaves him plenty of leisure time – and ample surplus energy – to enjoy himself. Since he can't spend the day and night watching TV game shows and soap operas, he devotes some of this leisure time to sex. We could do the same, if we tore ourselves away from the things which crowd our day, like work, commuter travelling, newspapers and television. Ovid, one of the earliest authorities on love, recognised that long-distance travelling killed passion, and in fact advocated it as a sedative remedy for Romans suffering from eroto-mania.

Sexual activity always soars when there is a power failure and people have to find other things to do than watch TV. When Chicago was enveloped in a blizzard, and people were stranded in their homes for days on end, pregnancies soared by 20 per cent.

Nowadays we live vicariously, relying on television to provide us with our adventures, friendships and romance. Every year on prime-time US television there are over 9,000 sex acts, according to statistics collected by the Planned Parenthood Federation of America.[10] This far exceeds the amount of sex most people experience in reality in an entire lifetime.

We are in grave danger of becoming a nation of voyeurs, rather than active, sexual participants. The existence of so much trash on television proves that couples will generally look at anything rather than each other. We spend more time glued to the box than clinging to each other.

You Can't Hurry Love

We live in a world of fast food, rapid results, quick fixes and instant coffee – and we want our sexual gratification to be equally instantaneous. We came, we saw, we climaxed. A ten-minute trip to ecstasy, where most of the time is taken up with the pre-coital formalities ('Your place or mine?') and the post-coital assessment. ('Did you make the big "O"?') There is no doubt that books, food, milk and sex *can* be condensed, but generally not without a loss of quality.

The sex act can be rushed, but not the process of sexual arousal. Mae West once told the world that she had made love to a man called Ted for a fifteen-hour stretch. To aid her enjoyment of these long love-ins she had her bedroom ceiling covered with mirrors. It was her belief that where sex is concerned, you can't have too much of a good thing.

It takes time to build a sexual relationship and time is the one thing we seem to have in short supply. Time has become our enemy rather than our friend. When the marriage of Masters and Johnson broke up, one of their co-workers explained: 'The tragedy is they didn't take the advice they gave their patients, which is to give time to their relationship.'

Masters and Johnson were undoubtedly innovative sex therapists, although they are wrongly credited as the inventors of several treatments they merely helped to popularise. The 'squeeze technique', which they employed with such success in the treatment of premature ejaculation, was first described by Dr James Semans in 1955. And the technique of 'sensate focusing', which they used to help patients forget their inhibitions and worries and concentrate of the sensuous 'here and now', had been used for years. But they did introduce one highly original treatment: the fourteen-day therapeutic holiday, during which clients concentrated their entire time and energy on enhancing their sex lives. This is a therapy which everyone can employ.

Sexercise 13

The Second Honeymoon

We go away for weekends to improve our golf, why not a few days to enhance our skill as lovers? A second honeymoon when we can take a rest from our everyday chores and devote our time to leisurely loving. One study of holidaymakers visiting Brampton Island, near the Australian Barrier Reef, revealed that 12 per cent were suffering a 'loss of sexual interest' at the start of their holidays, a figure which was halved after only four days of rest and peace.[11]

Try to take a regular recuperative break – say once a quarter – and you'll notice an improvement in your general health as well as your sex drive. This applies whatever your age, for as one geriatrician observed: 'A rested body enhances sexual desire and improves sexual performance as well as contributing to general health and well-being.'[12]

SUMMARY

- Stress can lower your output of sex hormones and decrease your libido. If you're going through a period of emotional strain, or heavy work pressures, earmark regular times when you can rest and relax – then you'll recapture your old sex drive.
- Don't limit your love-making to the fag end of the day, when you may be worn out by work and worry. Enjoy it while you're fresh, maybe after your morning coffee if you're not working, when your sex hormones are likely to be circulating at peak levels.
- If you're working to a tight schedule, find time to love. Don't allow yourself to become a spectator at life's rich feast. Why be a voyeur? Why watch sex on television when you could be enjoying the real thing?
- Take a holiday, even if it's only a brief weekend, for this will often help you regain your zest for life and lust for loving.

Fourteen

Fit as a Fiddle and Ready for Love

Anyone who wants to improve their athletic performance expects to benefit from fitness training. Boxers skip, discus-throwers lift weights, swimmers work out in the gym and footballers spend hours in circuit training. Today even sedentary artists, like concert pianists and chess grand masters, recognise the benefit of aerobic exercise. Why, then, is it not more widely recommended as a way of improving *sexual* performance?

Is it because we are always looking for overnight cures – love potions, hormonal injections or aphrodisiac pills – which will give our libido a quick boost? Surely we recognise that success is never instantaneous. Some of our greatest treasures – wisdom, gardens, friendships and grandchildren – take years to acquire. Can we not devote a few hours to the task of getting ourselves fit for love? The maintenance of sexual vitality is one of the seven major reasons for taking physical exercise – the other six don't matter.

Pick Yourself Up

When you're in tip-top physical condition sex is exhilarating; when you're in a low state of health it's an effort, and even potentially hazardous.

Many unfit men have heart attacks while they're on the job. This gives them the unique opportunity to come and go at the same time. Napoleon grew fat and flabby in his middle age and as a result suffered a marked loss of virility. Josephine complained to her friends that he was *bon à rien* (good for nothing) and once likened him to Crescentini, a famous castrato singer of the day. But Boney wasn't totally impotent, and on those occasions when he wasn't available to his spouse – 'Not tonight Josephine' – he took his pleasure with young girls. On one of these occasions the exertion proved too much and the Emperor passed out. The young girl, a sixteen-year-old actress called Mademoiselle

121

George, panicked and pulled the bell rope to summon the palace staff. A few minutes later Napoleon recovered, to find himself still in bed with the young girl, surrounded by a crowd of worried onlookers, including his wife.

Lord Palmerston suffered an even worse fate. He met his death on the top of a billiard table in his stately home, Brocket Hall, while he was seducing one of his young parlourmaids.

Unfit men like Bonaparte and Palmerston are at risk if they attempt to have sex, especially with a mistress rather than their wife. Surveys carried out in Japan show that eight out of ten cases of sudden death during intercourse arise in the course of extra-marital liaisons. To live for love is splendid; but to die for it seems a trifle excessive.

The Victorians tried to sublimate their sexual energy by taking vigorous physical exercise. This rarely worked, for even marathon runners, unless they drive themselves to the point of total exhaustion, find that activity enhances their sex drive. In 1919 a major in the British army wrote to his grandson giving him some standard advice to help him overcome the 'vice' of masturbation. 'Throw yourself into some extra hard work,' the letter suggested, 'get a long day on the golf links, or a good tramp across the Surrey commons.' The advice was therapeutically valueless, and the episode merits a mention only because of the major's pay-off line, which contained a delightful, unwitting *double entendre*: 'The remedy for this solitary vice lies in your own hands.'

Every Which Way but Loose

Most modern sex boutiques sell illustrated wall charts depicting 120 different coital positions. These should carry a government health warning. Most of the poses are suitable for contortionists and adagio dancers, but not for people with stiff muscles and arthritic spines. As an osteopath, my idea of safe sex has nothing to do with wearing a condom, it's about maintaining a reasonable degree of spinal flexibility.

More people slip a disc having sex than humping sacks of coal. 'How did it happen?' I ask when patients crawl into my consulting-rooms bent like hairpins. When the injury occurred in bed, or on the living-room floor, some look embarrassed. Others resort to downright lies, or conceal their discomfiture behind euphemisms like: 'I was having a spot of rough and tumble with my wife.'

One of my older patients told me a typical tale recently. He'd been married for forty years and thought that he'd given his wife her greatest ever sexual thrill. At the moment of climax she gave out an ecstatic cry.

That's it, he thought, I've made it. She's had the big 'O' at last. Seconds later she crawled out of bed and it was only then that he realised she'd been stricken with a particularly painful bout of cramp. At other times sexual high jinks can provoke more serious, long-lasting injuries such as sciatica.

Simon Forman was a contemporary of Shakespeare and a very popular London astrologer and physician. He kept a detailed and intimate diary, which revealed that when he was not casting horoscopes or treating patients, he liked to 'halek', which was his code-name for copulation. Unfortunately, his enthusiasm outstripped his physical fitness, and one day when he was having a particularly energetic romp with his young nurse he records: 'A pain took me in my left thigh in the sinews under the buttocks . . . and troubled me that I could not sleep nor stand that day.'[1] That fate can befall anyone who 'haleks' when they're not sufficiently supple. (Yoga is an excellent form of exercise for maintaining joint flexibility.)

Many wives seek medical advice about their partner's health. 'With my husband's angina/asthma/high blood pressure/rheumatism/bad back/smoker's cough, should we be having sex?' they ask. The answer is usually: 'Yes, with caution.' But what could be more inhibiting than sex with caution? How can a wife be abandoned if she thinks that at any moment her mate will blow a gasket, slip a disc or flip his lid? His agonising grunts and groans may bring out the mother in her, but what self-respecting man wants to make love to his mother?

Wasted Days, Wasted Nights

Lack of fitness is a barrier to optimum sexual fulfilment, as sex therapists through the years have recognised. Marie Stopes believed that physical fitness was the best possible aphrodisiac. 'Spend long days out of doors in healthful but not too exacting exercise,' was her recommendation.[2] Shere Hite, in the course of her survey, also had cause to stress the importance of physical fitness for middle-aged men. One forty-year-old executive told her that he had woken up to the fact that his sedentary lifestyle had impaired his health to the point where he had almost become a semi-invalid. So he took himself in hand, by doing some stretching exercises and taking regular walks around the block. The effects at first were painful, but the results 'dramatic'. 'My sexual feelings and ability have returned rapidly, plus the ability to breathe more comfortably. I'm beginning to think that what I thought were my sexual problems are more physical than I realised.'[3]

Unfortunately, this is a cure which few people seem prepared to take. This was the conclusion of two London psychologists who sought to find some way of increasing people's libido. The popular aphrodisiacs – Spanish fly, oysters, caviar and cannabis – they found useless or harmful. They considered 'stopping smoking, taking an interest in erotica and trying to improve one's general health' of limited value. Their 'best buy' was fitness training. This had enriched the sex lives of countless people. 'However,' they concluded somewhat gloomily, 'since most men would consider taking an early-morning run round the local park to be too drastic a step to take in the interests of their libido, the optimistic search for a true aphrodisiac is bound to continue.'[4]

Whole Lotta Love

Numerous surveys have shown the erotic effect of fitness training. A 1988 poll revealed that two-thirds of runners, and an equal percentage of cyclists, found that taking up regular aerobic exercise made them better lovers. A more detailed survey was carried out for a women's fitness magazine. Most of the women replying were exercising at least three times a week. Four out of ten reported that they were more easily aroused since they'd made the effort to get themselves fit. A third had sex more often, and a quarter reported that they climaxed more quickly.[5]

A similar effect is seen in competitive athletes, according to a German professor who studied the intimate sex lives of 800 sportsmen competing in the Munich Olympics. He found them a randy lot who, despite their heavy training schedules, still found the time and strength for sex, three to five times a week. The same is true of top British athletes, in the experience of Dr Craig Sharp, chief medical adviser to the 1972 British Olympic team. He tells of a middle-distance runner, hungry for sex, who had intercourse and then an hour later set a world record at his event. Another of his charges worked off his surplus energy in bed and then recorded a personal best on the track, running a mile in under four minutes.[6]

Some fun runners plaster the rear windows of their cars with stickers boasting: 'Joggers make better lovers' or 'Joggers can keep it up for hours'. There appears to be some truth in these proud claims. One case has gone on record of a young couple who entered a marathon on a miserable day and got increasingly aroused as the race proceeded. After a few miles of running side by side their mounting excitement and pheromone-laden sweat proved irresistible and they 'veered off into the

124

fog-shrouded bushes to prove that runners, indeed, do make better lovers.'[7] Since reading that account I now can't help but cast a quizzical eye over every marathon report. 'Four hundred gathered at the starting line; 284 finished.' Is *that* what happened to the other 116?

Keep Young and Beautiful

The nice thing about the physical fitness approach to improving sexual performance is that it has so many spin-off benefits. An impotent man can use a penile splint to prop up his flagging member, but it doesn't do much for his general health, and even less for his self-esteem. The person who is fit is more vivacious and looks more attractive sexually. This is important when making first contacts, especially for women, who are likely to remain wallflowers if they are grossly unfit or overweight. Arnold Schwarzenegger stated the problem clearly, with more candour than charm: 'I could have a relationship with a woman who is not into her body,' he conceded. 'But what is she going to look like in thirty years if she doesn't work out? And how can a husband be turned on if his wife is sitting like a slug stuffing herself with pastries?'

Researchers have found that the number of dates a young woman gathers is directly proportional to her attractiveness.[8] Masculine sex appeal is somewhat different, being based less on physical appearance than on economic ability and leadership skills. Nevertheless, men don't improve their romantic chances if they're fat and flabby. (The only good thing about a middle-aged spread is that it brings couples closer together.) A smoker's cough, bad breath, lethargy and a leaden gait are other definite turn-offs.

Sex appeal is easy to recognise, but difficult to define. It's associated with such things as vivacity, sparkling eyes and a clear skin, all of which are indicators of good health. Given these vibrant qualities it's generally easy to compensate for a hooked nose or receding chin. As Chesterton said: 'Give me ten minutes and I'll talk away my face.' (It would have taken him much longer – every bit of half an hour – to talk away his extreme obesity.)

Poor physical fitness also ushers in changes which mimic the ageing process, such as weakness, stiffness, lack of stamina, flabbiness and shortage of breath. These too are passion-killers. One lady in a geriatric hospital had a great desire to expose herself to the male inmates. One night she plucked up courage, took off her flannelette nightie and ran naked through the men's ward. 'Did you see what I saw?' said one startled patient.

125

'Yes,' said his friend in the next bed. 'It looked like Mavis Jenkins.'

'That's what I thought,' the other replied. 'I don't know what she was wearing, but it certainly needed ironing.'

Reactions like that are not conducive to sexual arousal.

It's possible to get rid of some of these creases by plastic surgery, but this can make your skin so tight that you have to bend your knees to smile. Besides, nips and tucks can alter your appearance, but will do nothing to improve your performance. You can use make-up to conceal your age, but you can't fool the flight of stairs which takes you up to your lover's bed. There's no substitute for physical fitness if you want to improve your appearance, appeal and erotic performance.

My Resistance is Low

There is evidence that other features of our contemporary lifestyle, such as smoking, breathing stale air and living indoors, have an adverse effect on our health and sexual vitality.

The link between smoking and reduced libido has been known for generations. At the very beginning of the seventeenth century Sultan Mourach banned the use of tobacco because it reduced the virility of Turkish men. (For some while smoking was an offence which carried the death sentence in Turkey. Punishments elsewhere were less severe. Persians caught in the act had their mouths filled with boiling oil, and Russians were likely to be flogged and sometimes castrated, which did even less for their virility.)

Recent evidence suggests that the Sultan's fears were fully justified. Experiments reveal that the blood levels of the male sex hormone testosterone rise when men quit smoking. Smokers also have lower sperm counts, with sperms that are less mobile and more likely to be malformed.

Reports from around the world clearly suggest that if men have the tenacity to quit smoking, their sex lives will improve. Doctors in France have found that the sexual activity of men who smoke heavily is considerably lower than that of non-smokers or men who smoke only the occasional cigarette. Quitting smoking can recharge libido. This has been the experience in America, where many people attending anti-smoking clinics report that their enjoyment of sex has increased since they gave up cigarettes. According to Dr Alton Ochsner, one of the pioneers and foremost advocates of these clinics: 'The ironic thing is that many men don't recognise that they have a libido problem until after they stop smoking, and then they realise what they've been missing.'

Inhaling bracing sea or mountain air can also invigorate your sex life. People living and working in centrally heated homes and offices spend their time inhaling air which carries an excess of positively charged particles. This has a lowering effect on many bodily functions.

Spring is in the Air

Our well-being and sexual vitality can often be boosted by moving to an environment where there is a preponderance of negative ions. Fred Soyka was a successful executive working for a multinational American company. While still in his twenties he was posted to Geneva, where he was soon made executive vice-president of the company's Swiss branch. From that moment onwards his health deteriorated. He became tense, tired, anxious and depressed. Worse still, his interest in sex waned. His local GP had met this syndrome before, especially among new arrivals to the town, who often suffered a loss of sexual interest and drive. 'I think there's something electrical about the air here in Geneva,' he surmised.

Soyka followed up this clue and realised that his symptoms were worse during the time of the *föhn*, the wind that carries a mass of positively charged ions. He studied research reports which demonstrated a clear link between sexual function and air ionisation. Trials showed that releasing negative ions into the air increased the fertility and sexual activity of mice.

The cause of Fred Soyka's problems seemed clear. He was one of the many ion-sensitive people. Geneva did not suit him because it is situated in a plain, where the Italian and Swiss Alps converge to form a V-shaped funnel. In situations like this there tends to be an accumulation of positive ions, which can sap both stamina and drive. The answer in his case was simple, as he relates in his book *The Ion Effect*.[9] He met a sales manager who had installed a table-top negative ion generator in his home in Lugano. This had made him feel more energetic and alert. But 'the biggest effect has been on my sex life' he confessed. 'My wife loves it.' Soyka adopted this remedy with gratifying results. Now it's recommended by sex therapists such as Dr Paul Pearson, Director of Education at the internationally renowned Kinsey Institute. He argues: 'The increase in respiration during sex can result in either more "bad" or more "good" air going in. For your own sex clinic, I suggest you place a tested, high-quality air ioniser . . . Opening a window and letting in some fresh air for sex can help, too.'[10] (For information on how to obtain an air ioniser see page 210.)

Marie Stopes was another great advocate of fresh air as a cure for sexual lassitude, especially when it was combined with liberal doses of ultraviolet light. 'The best aphrodisiac is bright sunlight,' she claimed.

Once again there is now a wealth of scientific evidence to substantiate her claim, which will be discussed in greater detail in chapter 15.

Madame de Pompadour was the favourite mistress of Louis XV of France. She was witty and vivacious, but 'excessively cold in matters of physical love', according to Madame du Husset, her personal maid and long-time companion. Fearing that she might lose the King's affection she started taking an aphrodisiac elixir, which brought her out in a rash. As an alternative she adopted a 'heating' diet, rich in peppers and spices, which she was told would help to inflame her passion. Instead it upset her delicate constitution. In desperation she consulted Dr Quesnay, her personal physician. He advised her that to achieve her goal she 'must try to be in good health, to digest well and, for that purpose, to take exercise'. The remedy obviously worked, because a short time afterwards she was able to confide to her maid: 'Our master is better pleased with me.'[11]

Sexercise 14
Dr Quesnay's Cure

Dr Quesnay's remedy is non-specific. It doesn't matter what physical exercise you take, providing it improves your well-being, stamina and physical vitality. A brisk half-hour's walk a day is a splendid tonic, suitable for people of all ages, which requires no special equipment or lengthy training. Set yourself the target of getting fit, by whatever means you choose, and your libido will increase.

The other ideal exercise is sex itself. Many women report that sex is addictive. The more you have, the more you want. Conversely the less you have, the less interested you become. 'If I go without sex for one month, then going six months is easy,' confessed one. Another noted: 'My sexual desire seems to decrease without sexual activity.'

Some authorities have suggested that regular performance improves the sexual apparatus, strengthening the pelvic muscles and causing 'work hypertrophy' of the clitoris. This is in accord with the Law of Use propounded by Hippocrates, which states: 'That which is used develops; that which is not used wastes away.' In other words, use it or lose it.

In bed, as in the jungle, it is always the fittest who survive.

SUMMARY

- Get yourself fit by embarking on a regime of regular exercise – brisk daily walking, swimming, dancing or tennis – for surveys show that people who take up aerobic exercise become better lovers.
- If you're a smoker, try to reduce your consumption of cigarettes. This will often produce a gradual, but quite appreciable, boost in libido.
- If you're one of the people who feel sluggish when they're in an environment of stale air, try to spend more time in the open air and in rooms with fresh air ventilation. This will boost your energy levels. You may also find it helpful to install a negative ion generator in your bedroom.

Fifteen

Doing What Comes Naturally

Fat people often attribute their flabbiness to glandular imbalance. This is generally no more than a face-saving excuse, for the only glands involved in obesity are normally the digestive glands. We get fat because we eat too much and exercise too little. In the same way many erotopenic subjects choose to believe that their lack of sex drive is caused by glandular failure. They are sexually listless because they have under-performing ovaries or testicles. This is rarely true. We may lack libido because we are anxious, tired, unfit, inhibited or unduly stressed, but seldom because our sex glands are defective.

You're Driving Me Crazy

There are several body chemicals which have an influence on sex drive, but by far the most important is testosterone, the hormone secreted by the male testes, the female ovaries and by the outer layer of the adrenal glands of both sexes. This is the hormone which turns boys into men and which also gives women their sex drive. If a female monkey is deprived of her testosterone-secreting glands she loses all interest in the opposite sex, but the romantic urge returns the moment she is given the hormone by injection. A similar effect is seen in human females. Their libido in increased by testosterone injections, a treatment commonly prescribed for female frigidity.

It's also noteworthy that blood testosterone levels in women are generally highest around the middle of the menstrual cycle. This is normally the time of peak sexual activity, a convenient arrangement since it is also the time of ovulation and therefore of maximum fertility. (Some early studies suggested that female sexual activity was at its height immediately prior to menstruation; but these surveys were made before the arrival of the birth control pill, when women were playing Vatican roulette and limiting intercourse to a time when they were least likely to conceive.)

A team of doctors and psychologists working for the Human Sexuality Program at the Mount Sinai School of Medicine, New York has shown that men with reduced libido have significantly lower than average blood levels of testosterone. The men who volunteered for this study spent four nights in a sleep laboratory. During this time they had catheters inserted in their arms so that samples of blood could be taken at hourly intervals while they slept. Their penises were also fitted with strain gauges to measure variations in their volume and state of erection. In addition they were quizzed in depth about their sex lives. The results demonstrated a clear link between testosterone and sexual behaviour. The men with the low hormonal levels of testosterone were less active sexually and showed reduced monthly rates of masturbation and attempted intercourse. In addition it was found that men with low hormone levels, who found it difficult to get an erection by day, also showed less sign of spontaneous penis activity during the night. By comparison with a control group of normal men their penises became erect less often, their increase in size was smaller, they became limp more rapidly and they swelled to their maximum girth only half as often.[1]

Feel Like Making Love

There is also evidence that testosterone is closely associated with pleasure-seeking behaviour, at least among laboratory animals. Rabbits which are wired up so that they can activate the pleasure centres of their brain normally can't get enough of these electric thrills. But their interest wanes if the males are castrated, or if either sex is given injections of drugs which block testosterone production.[2]

It's a Rich Man's World

If testosterone is so important for our happiness and sexual vigour, is it worth taking it as a regular medicine? This is a remedy many have tried. The craze was started more than a century ago by an eminent French doctor, Charles Edouard Brown-Sequard, who noticed a marked decline in his libido and physical health as he approached his seventieth birthday. To combat his increasing weakness he made the bold experiment of injecting himself with extracts of guinea pig testicles. The effect was startling. After only three injections his potency and muscular power returned.

Soon afterwards he was due to address the Société de Biologie. The date – 1 June 1889 – is held by some to be the birthday of the modern science of endocrinology. On this day the Professor startled his elderly audience with the dramatic way he chose to open his oration. 'I have always thought that the weakness of old men was partly due to the diminution of the function of their sexual glands,' he told them. 'I am seventy-two years old. My natural vigour has declined considerably in the past ten years.' He then proceeded to relate his experiments with the guinea pig gland injections. 'I have rejuvenated myself by thirty years and today I was able to pay a visit to my young wife.'

The French popular papers wasted no time in publicising the *méthode Sequardienne*, and even campaigned for funds to found an Institute of Rejuvenation. The good doctor progressed to making his extracts from the testicles of the bull, a beast with a reputation for virility far greater than that of the timorous guinea pig. This elixir he 'pumped into the gluteus maximus of thousands of aged but still libidinous *boulevardiers*.'[3] But the scientific world was not impressed and dismissed his experiments as 'senile aberrations' and 'further proof of the necessity of retiring professors who have attained their threescore years and ten.'

Subsequent tests showed that the injections were valueless, containing saline solution but not a trace of sex hormones. Brown-Sequard was disgraced. His young wife left him and soon afterwards he suffered a fatal stroke, brought on by trying to hurry up a flight of stairs.

Despite this setback the *méthode Sequardienne* retained its popularity with men of influence and means, such as Adolf Hitler, who were desperate to regain their flagging virility.

The remedy enjoyed a revival under the patronage of Dr Serge Voronoff, a colourful Russian aristocrat who was personal physician to the Khedive of Egypt. While serving at the royal court he noticed that a disproportionate amount of his time was taken up treating the petty ailments of the eunuchs who guarded the king's harem. He postulated that their premature ageing, and predisposition to sickness, was due to the fact that their castration had left them deficient in testosterone.

To test this theory, when he returned to Europe he started a series of experiments in which he 'rejuvenated' elderly rams and bulls by giving them transplants taken from the testes of young, healthy animals. He announced his results on 18 October 1919 at an excited meeting of the French Surgical Congress, and was immediately besieged by elderly men eager to receive testicular transplants taken from virile young chimpanzees. The expensive treatment didn't work because the transplants were quickly rejected by the body's immune system. The patients were poorer but physically no better. Yet this did little to damage

Voronoff's reputation or his lifestyle, which blossomed when his wealthy American wife died, leaving him rich and free to marry a Romanian princess forty years his junior.

Paul de Kruif, the American writer, was a later advocate of rejuvenation by hormone replacement therapy. To him it was as natural for men to preserve their youth by taking testosterone as for diabetics to maintain their lives by taking insulin. Towards the twilight of his life he took 20 or 30 milligrams of methyl testosterone a day, and justified the practice in his book *The Male Hormone*: 'I'm not ashamed that it's no longer made to its old degree by my own ageing body. It's chemical crutches. It's borrowed manhood. It's borrowed time. But just the same, it's what makes bulls bulls.'[4]

Whether Kruif retained his bull-like potency we do not know. Certainly the vast majority of doctors, while they may advocate hormone replacement therapy for women, are sceptical of its use for men.

As men age they suffer a gradual decrease in testosterone output, a decline which begins the moment they cease to be teenagers. This is accompanied by a steady decline in sexual function. The frequency of intercourse, the intensity of orgasm and the speed of achieving an erection all suffer a slow but relentless reduction. The force of ejaculation is also curtailed, a young man being capable of shooting his semen a full 2 feet, compared with the mere 6 inches of an older man. But although these changes occur at roughly the same time, there is no evidence that they are in any way linked. As they grow older men become greyer, stiffer and more forgetful, but nobody suggests that this is due to a loss of sex hormones. Bodily functions decline as an integral part of the ageing process, and as yet there is no known chemical or hormone which can ensure perpetual youth.

The vast majority of elderly men have blood levels of testosterone which are well above the threshold needed to support a healthy sex life. For them it is pointless to supercharge their bloodstream with additional hormones, since this is unlikely to have any effect whatsoever on their sexual performance.

Athletes of both sexes today are taking testosterone and other anabolic steroids to boost their muscle bulk. These drugs have been outlawed, not simply because they encourage unfair competition, but also because they can cause adverse side-effects, such as high blood pressure, liver disorders, heart disease, glandular problems and cancer of the liver and kidneys. Testosterone therapy is also available in a growing number of sex therapy clinics. These flourishing medical ventures offer men a cure for impotence and flagging virility and a veiled promise of eternal youth. The dosage of steroids used in these clinics is generally much less than that used by body-builders and athletes, but it still carries risks and should be undertaken only with the sanction of your personal physicians.

The Best Things in Life are Free

Besides, there are other ways of increasing testosterone output which are natural, safe and free. Some have been mentioned already. Being a voyeur, and looking at sexually arousing films, is likely to increase the output of testosterone.[5] So too will being an actual participant in sexual fun and games. This was shown when volunteers were trained to take samples of their own blood during times of erotic activity. When the specimens were analysed it was found that testosterone levels were raised during times of sexual arousal and also immediately after coitus. This bears out what was said at the end of the last chapter, that there is nothing like sex to enhance sexual performance.

Feedback neural loops exist which send messages from the brain to the testosterone-secreting glands, and also from the glands to the brain's sex centres. Travelling in the one direction it is testosterone which excites the limbic area of the brain and prepares the body for sexual activity; following the reverse pathway it is the brain's sex centres which stimulate the secretion of the sex glands.

Physical exercise is another natural way of increasing the output of sex hormones. This was confirmed by a team of Australian doctors, who found that plasma testosterone levels rose when men took part in vigorous sports like rowing, cycling and swimming. They also noted that the elevation of hormone levels, which usually lasted for about an hour, was accompanied by an increase in sexual activity and desire.[7]

It Ain't What You Do

In this, as in most other health practices, it is vital to observe the ancient warning 'everything in moderation'. Too little exercise can dampen sexual ardour, but then so too can too much. This was confirmed by studies carried out at Los Condores University, California. These showed that testosterone levels and sexual activity rose steadily when people jogged a reasonable distance of 5 to 15 miles a week, but then declined quite rapidly as they clocked up greater mileages. The comparison was most marked between the modest exercisers (15 miles a week) and the serious, marathon runners (120 miles a week) The former had average testosterone levels which were 16 times higher than the latter, and sexual activity scores which were 9 times greater.[8]

So far nobody knows for certain what causes the sharp fall in hormone output, which is often now called the Condores Effect. Some believe it is brought about by overheating the testicles; others by shock waves reverberating through the body, which give the skull a thump approximately equal to the weight of the body every time the foot strikes the ground. This regular pounding may traumatise the brain cells and impair the function of the pituitary gland. Whatever the exact cause, Professor Alex Horowicz, who led the Los Condores study, warns: 'There is no doubt that after prolonged running a man is not at the height of his sexual prowess.'

Following this caution, some Californian drivers have removed their car stickers claiming that 'Joggers keep it up for hours'. In their place they now display the justified warning: 'Too much jogging makes you limp'.

Sex drive can also be reduced by eating meat contaminated with oestrogen. Many farmers still fatten their chickens and beef cattle by supplementing their feed with oestrogen and other banned steroid drugs, such as clenbuterol, or 'angel dust'. This is a cheap way of adding to their bulk, which is capable of increasing a cow's weight by 17 pounds a day. Governments have tried with little success to minimise the extent of this abuse, which is believed to be rife. A recent European Commission report into the scandal was hushed up, but a Belgian politician has reported that up to 80 per cent of his country's meat output is now contaminated by steroidal hormones.

That's My Weakness Now

The repeated ingestion of minute quantities of oestrogen can reduce libido in a quite dramatic way, as the male inhabitants of an Italian seaside resort discovered. They had always been proud of their virility and their ability to pleasure the visiting lady tourists, and so were shocked when they found themselves becoming increasingly impotent. Even their appearance became effeminate as over a period of several months they started to develop breasts and lose their facial hair. Two doctors were called in to investigate the problem, and identified the cause quite fortuitously as they took a bite of chicken breast at a local *trattoria*. Inside they found a tiny pellet of oestrogen. Searching through other chicken samples they found the same incriminating objects, which had been implanted by the owner of a nearby chicken farm to fatten up his birds. As soon as the men stopped eating the tainted meat their sex drive recovered.

A Hard Man is Good to Find

Activities which decrease the production of testosterone, such as tiredness, stress, smoking and excessive exercise, should obviously be avoided. Their place should be taken by measures which help to boost the production of the libido hormone, like *moderate* exercise and erotic stimulation. Two further hormone-boosting procedures follow, both of which are of considerable antiquity.

For generations there has been a belief that cold baths increase sex drive. Dr Edward Baynard, an eighteenth-century British physician, observed that freshwater fishermen who stood for hours immersed up to their waists in icy water enjoyed high levels of erotic arousal. So he offered the treatment to some of his male patients who were suffering from what he coyly described as disorders of the 'codpiece economy'. The results were dramatic, according to his equally demure report, which told of 200 men who bathed in cold water and found that the treatment 'wound up their watch and set their pendulum in *status quo*'.[11]

More recently, geriatricians have made a study of the remarkably active centenarians living in the Caucasian mountains and have suggested that their virility may be linked to their habit of bathing in cold mountain streams and lakes. Studies carried out by Dr A. Fonarev, a Russian biologist, show that when the body is exposed to cold water, the surface blood vessels contract and so force blood inwards to the heart, brain and hormonal glands. The Georgian peasants expect to remain sexually active into their eighties and nineties, and Dr Fonarev suggests that by subjecting themselves to regular 'water fortification' they may have fortuitously discovered the fountain of youth.

Sexercise 15
Taking the Plunge
Cold water showers and baths have a powerful tonic effect and can increase metabolism by as much as 80 per cent. In men, the cold water treatment increases sperm production, and in both sexes it appears to stimulate the output of sex hormones. This was discovered when researchers at the the Thrombosis Research Institute in

London, invited a sample of a hundred volunteers to adopt a 'disciplined regime' of taking a daily cold bath. The results were described as 'astonishing'. Blood tests showed an increased output of sex hormones and a rise in the number of infection-combating white cells. One man, who was a victim of extreme fatigue and had been confined to bed for hours on end, found that his vigour was 'vastly improved'. Professor Vijay Kakkar, the Institute's director and himself a cold bath devotee, intends extending the researches but adds a word of caution: 'People must realise that this is not a cure for everything. But it is a way to make our bodies perform better.'[12]

Like Professor Kakkar, I enjoy the stimulus of a regular cold dip and warmly recommend it as a multi-purpose tonic. But if you do decide to take the plunge yourself, don't do it too abruptly. Acclimatise yourself slowly by taking showers of gradually cooler temperature before you expose yourself to the full Spartan regime. Spend no more than two or three minutes in the cold water and always finish up with a brisk rub down with a rough Turkish towel. This should leave your body glowing from head to foot. If you're left with chattering teeth, goose bumps and blue skin you've overdone the cold exposure and should take it easier next time. And a final word of caution: if you have a heart condition, or any other serious ailment which may affect your endurance, consult your doctor before you embark on the cold water treatment.

It may seem strange that cold baths, which were once imposed on public school boys to dampen their ardour and taken by medieval monks 'to rid them of worldly thoughts', should now be recommended as sexual stimulants. But the therapeutic *volte face* is commonplace. Fashions are as prevalent in medicine as they are in the world of *haute couture*. When I studied first aid as a youngster it was customary to treat muscle strains with hot water, 'to bring out the bruise'. Now the same injuries are treated with cold water to contract the blood vessels within the muscles and so limit the extent of the bleeding. Years later, when I studied medicine, patients who'd suffered heart attacks were urged to take life easily to rest their hearts. Now they're encouraged to jog to strengthen their cardiac muscles.

The recipe which follows has been the subject of a similar therapeutic U-turn, which I believe will prove to have disastrous consequences. Soon after the end of the First World War, long before the advent of jogging and low-cholesterol foods, the world's number one health cult was sunbathing. In Denmark, Dr Neils Finsen received a Nobel prize for his pioneering work in the use of heliotherapy in the treatment of skin complaints. Dr A. Rollier gained international acclaim for his success in treating childhood tuberculosis is his 'school in the sun' in the Swiss Alps. About the same time in Britain Dr Edward Mellanby publicised his discovery that rickets is a deficiency disease which can be prevented by exposure to natural or artificial sunlight.

These exciting medical discoveries launched a worldwide sunbathing craze. Nudist colonies sprang up overnight. Actinotherapy clinics were opened in all the major industrial centres to give sick city children the benefit of the sun's healing rays. Solariums were opened at pit heads so that sun-starved miners could have their share of ultraviolet light. Schoolchildren took their classes in the open air. Shipping lines offered special sunshine cruises. The Riviera, which had once been a purely winter resort, now became a summer playground for European sun-seekers. Open-necked shirts and shorts were the order of the day. Everywhere people basked in the sun.

The medical profession was happy then to agree with the old English proverb, 'The sun is the best physician, but the most difficult to make an appointment with.' In recent years these views have been subject to dramatic revision. Today we are told to avoid the sun's rays for fear of developing skin cancer. Now is not the time to argue the merits or demerits of this remarkable judgement, except to say that the evidence clearly shows that *sensible* exposure to the sun's rays, encouraging gentle tanning but not burning, remains an invaluable health aid. It stimulates metabolism, cleanses the skin of harmful bacteria, increases the blood's white cell count, strengthens the bone texture by encouraging the formation of vitamin D and boosts sexual vitality.

Biologists have known that sunlight affects the sexual behaviour of animals for well over half a century. When stickleback fish are exposed to sunlight they show an increase in their output of sex hormones. Hamsters suffer a shrinking of their testes, sometimes to a quarter of their normal size, when they are kept in darkness. In the same way birds which normally breed only in the spring can be encouraged to produce a second clutch of eggs in the winter if their bodies are bathed in ultraviolet light.

Sunlight is also a spur to human sexual behaviour as the record books show. Tennyson was wrong to suggest that it was in the spring that 'a young man's fancy lightly turns to thoughts of love'. We're most likely to feel amorous when our bodies are warmed by the sun's rays. This was confirmed by a study of over a million births in New York, which showed that the maximum number of conceptions occur at the end of the summer. Contrary to the Tennyson belief, spring is the time of the year when fewest babies are conceived. The sap may be rising then, at the end of the long, dark days of winter, but not lovers' passions.

Two Boston researchers have shown that exposing the skin to sunlight acts as a stimulus for testosterone production.[13] This explains why testosterone levels are higher in the middle of the day than in the morning and evening, and why they peak towards the end of the summer, levels being about a third higher in June than in the sun-starved days of February.

Sexercise 16
Actinic Power

Expose your body to the sun and you'll quickly increase your output of testosterone, which the Boston researchers found was doubled after a course of five ultraviolet treatments of gradually increasing dosage, each enough to produce mild reddening of the skin. The greater the area of skin exposed the greater the glandular stimulus. This means that when a bathing belle lazes topless on the beach she's not only increasing her eye appeal but also letting the watching world know that she's probably in the mood for love, with her bloodstream flooded with sex hormones.

Both sexes respond to this actinic stimulus, men slightly more strongly than women, and especially so if they expose their testicles to the sun's rays. This can triple the output of testosterone, compared with the doubling which occurs when the back alone is bared.

SUMMARY

- Don't be afraid to enjoy the stimulus of erotic pictures and videos, for this has been shown to boost the output of sex hormones.
- Don't allow yourself to become overtired. Sensible levels of physical exercise will increase your sex hormone levels, but the levels drop the moment you become fatigued. This is a risk for people who jog more than 30 miles a week, or take other forms of vigorous exercise.
- Avoid eating meat which has been artificially fattened by feeding the cattle on oestrogen.
- If you are in reasonably good health, try taking a regular cold bath or shower. This is another time-honoured way of boosting sex drive.
- Sex hormone levels can also be boosted by sunbathing. Do this regularly and judiciously, so that you do not blister or burn but develop a healthy overall tan.

Sixteen

Love Potion Number Nine

There's never been a shortage of aphrodisiac potions and pills. Most have been aimed at men suffering from 'lost manhood', a condition which does not rate a mention in orthodox medical textbooks but which appears to have been a combination of impotence and sexual apathy.

One popular remedy, Gordon's Sexual Restorative, was advertised as a 'viro-erectile elixir'. Another, which contained a mixture of glandular extracts and cantharides, was offered to every male who 'doesn't realise that he is not paying his wife the attention he formerly did', surely a vast target audience. A third was marketed by the Rev. Francis Bacon, an English priest who masqueraded under the name Dr Hannah Brown. His pills promised to give men the power to 're-enter paradise for five shillings'.

A Taste of Honey

Some of the world's most energetic Romeos took sexual stimulants. Errol Flynn, who died at fifty but boasted of having spent over 12,000 nights making love, enhanced his performance by applying a pinch of cocaine to the tip of his penis. King Farouk, who maintained harems at each of his five palaces and is reputed to have had intercourse with 5,000 different women, took aphrodisiac pills containing a mixture of caffeine, hashish and honey. The Marquis de Sade kept himself going during his prolonged, sadistic orgies by taking Spanish fly, and was once sentenced to death *in absentia* when two of the young girls he had beaten and repeatedly seduced suffered a fatal overdose of cantharides, which he had given them disguised in sweets heavily flavoured with aniseed.

These remedies have one thing in common – they don't work. Many are dangerous and most revolting to taste. Yet belief in their miraculous powers still persists in modern folklore, and their claims are often more difficult to swallow than the pills themselves. It seems that men will take the most bizarre mixtures if they believe they will boost their waning sexual powers. One farmer called in a vet when his bull failed to perform his duty. The vet carried out a quick inspection and then prescribed a medicine which he was sure would solve the problem. The results were dramatic. Within hours the bull regained its old friskiness and started pawing the ground and sniffing for female company. 'That was powerful medicine,' the farmer said as he related the tale to a gathering of the regulars at the village pub.

'What was it?' one of his friends asked.

'I don't really know,' he replied. 'But it tasted like liquorice.'

Ain't Misbehavin'

Potions have also been used to curb sexual desire. Roman men cooled their ardour by anointing their penises with mouse dung, or by eating the leaves of eunychion, a herb which Pliny described as the 'maker of eunuchs'.

For women the anaphrodisiac of choice was the shrub *vitex agnus castus*, better known as the tree of chastity. Athenian women spread its leaves over their bed to preserve their purity, especially during certain religious festivals during which they were required to abstain from sex for four or five days.

These remedies, like the sex stimulants, earned a fortune for their makers. The Rev. Dr Sylvester Graham tried to get his fellow Americans to wean themselves off meat and spicy food to cure their obsession with sex. Instead they were to eat wholesome Graham crackers. Dr John Kellogg was engaged on the same, highly lucrative, moral crusade when he struggled to get the US nation breakfasting on Kellogg's cornflakes rather than passion-raising bacon, eggs and ham.

During the Second World War there was a widespread belief that the sex drive of Allied troops was kept in check by secretly dousing their food with sedative drugs. One French soldier demanded that the army authorities should refund the 15 francs he'd wasted on a prostitute, because he was convinced that his army-issue wine had been doped with saltpetre which had made him impotent. This belief persisted for some years after the war, and when I served a brief spell in the Royal Air Force it was still thought that the libido of mixed sex units was artificially suppressed by dosing the NAAFI tea with bromide. As a result airmen often asked: 'Do you want a cup of tea, or are you hoping to go out on the town tonight?'

But neither bromide nor saltpetre kills sexual desire. This can be done more effectively by taking one of the many medically prescribed drugs which are known to depress sexual performance as an unwanted side-effect. These include sedatives and narcotics, such as diazepam, the tricyclic anti-depressants and monoamine oxidase inhibitors. Also oestrogen and anti-hypertensive agents containing reserpine and methyldopa. If you are taking regular medication, and think that it may be having an adverse effect on your sexual performance, seek your doctor's advice and see if you can change to another drug with less troublesome side-effects.

That's a Plenty

Alcohol is another depressant drug which can kill sexual passion. In small doses it may stimulate sexual activity by sedating the higher centres in the brain which inhibit sex drive. But in larger doses, as Shakespeare observed, it 'increases the desire but takes away the performance'. Male boozers often become impotent, developing an occupational hazard commonly known as 'brewer's droop'.

They can also suffer testicular degeneration, which a team of Pittsburg scientists attributed to an associated lack of vitamin A, or more especially of its derivative retinaldehyde, which is vital for testicular metabolism and sperm production. This lack can occur even in social drinkers, according to the researchers, who warn: 'The amounts of alcohol necessary for the inhibition of retinaldehyde formation appear to be well below the range of concentrations customarily found in alcoholic individuals.'[1]

Another experiment, carried out at the Mount Sinai School of Medicine, New York, showed that heavy drinkers suffer a marked drop in testosterone production. Within two days of drinking the equivalent of a daily bottle of spirits, the eleven male volunteers experienced a profound fall in hormone production. A month later, when the trial ended, their testosterone output had dropped to an average of 30 to 50 per cent of normal levels. In addition they showed a rise in oestrogen secretion, which may explain why male topers often become more feminine in their appearance, losing some of their body hair and putting on fat around their buttocks and breasts.[2]

Am I Wasting My Time?

It's safe to assume that the majority of people reading this book don't *want* to quench the flames of love by smoking, drinking to excess or swallowing sedative drugs. Most of us are keen for the erotic fires to burn a little brighter, and the perennial question is: can this be achieved by eating certain foods?

Over the years just about every dietary ingredient has been said to have aphrodisiac properties, from common foodstuffs like potatoes and tomatoes to the rarer delicacies such as oysters and caviare. Garlic is possibly the oldest reported sexual stimulant. Every Jewish male was expected to pleasure his wife on a Friday night. To give him strength, it was traditional for him to eat garlic on this day, for the Talmud assured him that 'garlic promotes love and arouses desire'.

In medieval Europe herbalists extolled the invigorating properties of orchid tubers. The belief in their aphrodisiac powers must be of considerable antiquity, for the word orchid is derived from the Latin for testicle. Some species have even been called *satyrion*, because it was thought that they were responsible for the wild, orgiastic behaviour of the satyrs.

Orchids were grown in vast quantities in America, where they were used by wanton women to make a loving cup which was said to have 'wrought the desired effect'. In Britain it was claimed that 'enough orchids grew in Cobham Park in Kent to pleasure all the seamen's wives in Rochester.'

Nowadays few people would think of taking orchids to boost their virility, but many still eat oysters, which are an equally ancient love potion. They were popularised by Casanova, Europe's most famous sexual athlete, who used them to sustain his potency during his long, amorous nights. He organised orgies, where oysters were passed from mouth to mouth, and had to be retrieved when they fell between 'alabaster spheres'.

Some think that oysters got their erotic reputation because their shape and texture are somewhat similar to the female pudenda, others because they are rich in potassium (in this case we should be taking Parmesan cheese, which contains nearly six times as much potassium as an equivalent weight of oysters).

One nervous bridegroom was anxious that he might not be able to cope on his wedding night. He asked the advice of his more experienced best man, who assured him that all would be well if he took a dozen oysters before he retired to bed. When the honeymoon was over the best man asked if the remedy had succeeded. 'Well, *quite* well,' the newlywed replied. 'I took the twelve oysters as you suggested, but only five of them worked.'

Eggs are another food said to increase venereal desire. They were the mainstay of Brigham Young, one of the founders of the Mormon

Church, who had at least fifty-three wives, who were lodged in separate cubicles on the second floor of his home in Salt Lake City. To enable him to satisfy their demands he ate large numbers of eggs, which he was convinced sustained his virility.

Cock-eyed Optimist

These ancient dietary prescriptions may be of little practical value, but they have the great advantage of being innocuous, which cannot be said of all aphrodisiacs.

Each night before they went to bed a research chemist gave his mistress a drug which he claimed caused 'a euphoria of excellent sexual relations'. One evening she felt unusually sexy and wanted to strip off her clothes in public. He took her home, gave her more of the same sex stimulant and made love to her twice. The next day she was dead, from an overdose of a drug which is freely available in most of today's 'swinging' cities. Some of these pills are described as 'sex enhancers'. One group contains substances such as amyl nitrite and isobutol nitrite, which are used in the standard treatment of anginal pain. When absorbed into the body, they dilate the blood vessels and can produce a powerful engorgement of the penis, which is why they are popular with homosexual male communities when sold under trade names such as 'Hardware'. The drugs are dangerous and can provoke widespread and fatal vascular collapse. They play no part in the quest for sexual rejuvenation, or in the treatment of erotopenia.

The same is true of Spanish fly, a powder containing cantharidin, derived from the bodies of blister beetles. This has been widely used throughout the world, being known in England as Spanish fly, as Russian fly in Eastern Europe, and as Hindu fly in most of the Arab-speaking countries. (It seems customary to blame foreigners for our sexual peccadillos: thus Englishmen referred to syphilis as 'the French pox', while the French called it 'the Spanish disease' and the Japanese the 'Chinese sickness'.) In small doses the cantharides cause irritation of the urethra, which is no doubt how they came to be regarded as genital stimulants. But in larger doses they give rise to internal bleeding, kidney damage, violent abdominal pain and sometimes even death.

The history books are full of tragedies caused by taking Spanish fly, but these have done little to destroy the cantharide legend, which was built up on anecdotal reports of the drug's wonder-working powers. One woman claimed that her husband, after taking Spanish fly, had copulated eighty-seven times in the space of two days. 'Forty times on end', was the astonished report of another wife. Although these accounts were reported in the medical press they are almost certainly fictitious. Most of the men involved were seriously ill after taking the drug, and a number died, which is the only part of the tale which merits serious belief. These drugs are lethal, which is no doubt why the Romans called love potions *venenum*, a Latin word which also means poison.

It's Witchcraft

Dangerous drugs like cantharides and amyl nitrite continue to be used because of people's desperate need to increase their sexual drive. The same urgent desire drives others to take exotic remedies like powdered shark fins, the gall bladders of bears and the pizzles (penises) of deer, which sell at exorbitant prices at folk markets throughout the world. They retain their popularity because they operate on the mind if not on the body. They instil faith and inspire hope, which is likely to bring about an improvement in sexual performance in about a third of cases, for this is the normal rate of placebo response. (In one trial, 10 per cent of men taking a placebo became impotent, because this was one of the side-effects of the pill they thought they were taking![3])

The current proliferation of aphrodisiacs is sure proof of their intrinsic worthlessness, for there is an ancient medical adage which says: 'The more remedies there are for any one complaint, the less faith can be put in any one of them.' This makes sense, for at one time there were scores of treatments for scurvy: now there is only one – vitamin C. This simple, safe and effective remedy has made all others superfluous.

In an age which has witnessed phenomenal growth in medical science can there really be no genuine aphrodisiac medication? That was one of the many vital questions I had to answer when I set out to compile this book.

Too Marvellous for Words

Most doctors skirt the question altogether. Since they have learned little or nothing at medical school about the pharmacological management of sexual lassitude, they assume that no such treatment exists. But is this true?

I searched the reference books and found hundreds of substances which were claimed to have aphrodisiac powers. They fell roughly into two categories. First there were a variety of vitamins and minerals, which were given to overcome states of nutritional deficiency and so improve general vitality and health. Then there was a vast array of herbal remedies which were claimed to have a direct effect on sexual performance. The choice was bewildering; the supporting scientific evidence scant and often confusing.

Some of the medicaments seemed to be based on little more than sympathetic magic. East African tribesmen eat the heart of a lion to become brave, and by the same token it is argued that men should eat the penis of a deer to gain the potency of the monarch of the glen. These remedies can be discarded immediately. So too can the recipes which are either untested or potentially dangerous. But this still leaves a shortlist of several dozen remedies which *might* have aphrodisiac powers. To evaluate these recipes I sought the help of a friend, Ronald Levin, a fellow of the Royal Pharmaceutical Society and member of the Nutrition Society. The basic question I posed was: 'Do these, or any other substances, have the ability to increase sexual arousal and drive?' We agreed at the outset that to be acceptable the remedies needed to be both safe and scientifically well attested.

The Food of Love

The early Christian saints were shrewd. When they wanted to conquer their lustful thoughts they put themselves on a starvation diet. They knew that they were far less likely to be tempted by the seductive charms of the local maidens when they were suffering from malnutrition. You have to be fit to be brimming over with sexual vitality. This was recognised by John Bunyan, who said that it is much more difficult to be virtuous when you are healthy.

Many people today are living on nutritionally inadequate diets which impair their health and reduce their sex drive. They eat unbalanced diets containing too much over-processed convenience food. As a result they run the risk of suffering a lack of certain essential vitamins and minerals. This lack often goes unrecognised for years, since the effects of suboptimal nutrition are invariably slow and insidious. But eventually the effects begin to be felt, and by the time they reach middle age many people on poor diets start to realise that they've lost their youthful zest and drive. They may not be suffering any recognisable disease, but are nevertheless existing in a state of sub-health. They are below par, listless, easily tired and lacking enthusiasm. In this one-degree-under state they can work up neither the interest nor the energy to lead a vibrant sex life.

'Modern science is now certain that nothing is so important to total vitality, which includes virility, as proper nutrition.' That was the judgement of two American authorities – one a medical geriatrician the other a sexologist – in a paper entitled 'Ageing and Sex.'[4] In this wide-ranging review they emphasise the importance of vitamin B in maintaining a healthy sex life.

This group of vitamins is vital for the transport and release of energy throughout the body. Under ideal conditions there need be no shortage of vitamin B1 (thiamine) or vitamin B2 (riboflavin); but how many people today are living in ideal conditions? An analysis of over twenty dietary studies in America suggests that half the US population may be deficient in thiamine and 40 per cent lacking in riboflavin. Heavy drinkers, and people with a sweet tooth, are prone to run short of riboflavin, large quantities of which are used up in the breaking down of carbohydrates such as alcohol and sugar. Deficiencies can also arise when people are under prolonged medication, especially with drugs such as antacids, sleeping pills, barbiturates and anti-seasickness pills.

Vigorous exercise can also provoke shortages, especially of thiamine, which is needed for the conversion of sugar into energy, and also for the excretion of the waste products of carbohydrate metabolism. Long-distance running can cause a fifteen-fold increase in the body's consumption of vitamin B1. Similar losses occur when people are under stress, which is why nutritionalists recommend that thiamine intake should be raised 700 per cent during periods of stress. Other problems arise from faulty eating patterns. All the members of the vitamin B group are soluble in water and so are easily destroyed by cooking. (For this reason foods should be as lightly cooked as possible; and full advantage taken of the water in which meat and vegetables are cooked, which makes a highly nutritious basis for soups, stocks and gravies.)

It is easy to see how shortages of vitamin B arise, especially among city dwellers who lead stressful lives, eat badly, drink too much alcohol and take an excessive amount of aerobic exercise in a vain attempt to restore their drooping fitness levels. These mild deficiency states are of no consequence, according to many physicians who take notice only when they become so severe that they give rise to gross deficiency diseases like beriberi. Milder shortages cause less obvious symptoms, such as irritability, fatigue and insomnia, which are states of dis-ease rather than specific medical diseases.

Experiments into the effects of vitamin B deficiency, carried out at Harvard University's Fatigue Laboratory, showed that the muscular efficiency of volunteers on a vitamin-impoverished diet was dramatically reduced when they were set to work on a treadmill. They tired more rapidly, and took longer than usual to recover from their exertions. Once their diet was supplemented with vitamin B, most of the subjects regained their previous level of physical fitness within a few days.

Vitamin B1 (thiamin) is derived from a wide variety of foods, but particularly rich sources are pork, beef, whole grains, brown rice, peas, beans and lentils. The richest sources of Vitamin B2 (riboflavin) are dairy products, meat (especially liver), cereals and green, leafy vegetables.

You can't be imbued with a zest for life, or a healthy lust for sex, if you're existing on a vitamin-impoverished diet. Nor can you expect to be overflowing with vitality if your diet lacks essential minerals.

Little Things Mean a Lot

Most of the tonics our parents took contained iron, the mineral which is essential for the formation of the body's red blood cells. It is estimated that 20 million Americans today suffer from iron deficiency anaemia, often without their knowledge. These victims are likely to be perpetually below par, chronically short of energy, stamina and strength and almost certainly lacking the necessary drive to enjoy an exciting love life. (This is a particular problem for women during their reproductive years, since 25 to 150 milligrams of iron are lost with every menstrual period.)

Zinc is another mineral closely related to sex drive, which is particularly likely to be deficient in the elderly, in people with bowel disease, who are taking diuretic drugs, who eat processed foods, drink to excess or are existing on fad diets, slimming regimes or foods rich in fibre. Every year thousands of research papers are written about zinc, which has been described as the 'most critical of the trace minerals', because it is involved in more than twenty of the body's vital enzyme systems.[5]

Estimates suggest that 20 per cent of British men are deficient in zinc, the mineral which Professor Derek Bryce-Smith of Reading University believes plays an important role in counteracting reduced sex drive and loss of male fertility. 'I am not claiming it is a panacea,' he writes in *Chemistry in Britain*, 'just that it has been neglected.'[6] The average Briton consumes only 67 per cent of the recommended daily intake of zinc and the risk of deficiency is particularly great in sexually active men, since 1 milligram of zinc is lost with every ejaculation.[7] As oysters are rich sources of zinc (and also iron and vitamin B2), this may be why they were so highly prized by sexual athletes like Casanova, who is reputed to have consumed fifty oysters a day.

On a well-balanced diet it's not necessary to take dietary supplements. That's the official medical view, which is ignored by most laymen and a large proportion of doctors. (A recent survey of almost 700 members of the Harvard Medical School faculty revealed that almost a quarter were taking vitamin and mineral supplements.[8])

Can people suffering from reduced sex drive benefit from taking any form of dietary supplementation? That was the multi-million dollar question that I asked Ronald Levin. As I expected, his reply was cautious. 'That will depend on the underlying cause of their reduced sex drive, which could be social, psychological or metabolic.' However, he recognised that our present lifestyle can lead to nutritional imbalance. In view of this, 'since many dietary components, such as vitamins and minerals, play a part in ensuring full metabolic efficiency, it makes sense to ensure a full daily complement'.

He also stressed the importance of the anti-oxidant vitamins – beta-carotene, vitamin C and vitamin E – in protecting against the metabolic diseases of old age, such as heart disease and cancer. 'These vitamins apparently neutralise the potentially damaging effect of free radicals and other highly reactive by-products of muscle metabolism.' They are safe to take and their value has been demonstrated in numerous, large-scale trials around the world.

Wake Up and Love

Of the very wide range of herbs claimed to have aphrodisiac powers, only two met with the Levin stamp of approval. The first, ginseng, has been used by the Chinese for thousands of years for its remarkable powers in prolonging youth and restoring lost sexual vigour. It was introduced to Europe early in the seventeenth century, and was popularised by Father Jartoux, a French Jesuit priest, who broadcast the fact that after taking ginseng he lost his tiredness and experienced a great surge in vitality.

Experiments with laboratory animals confirm that ginseng has the power to stave off fatigue and improve physical performance by 25 to 33 per cent. These researches are reviewed in *Stay Young*, a book written by Dr Ivan Popov, who has spent thirty years studying and practising revitalisation medicine. 'I have made numerous tests which confirm the plant's wide spectrum ability to act positively on physical as well as mental processes,' he writes. 'The activity of ginseng is long-lasting, and there are no withdrawal symptoms of any kind when it is interrupted. Side-effects and toxicity are apparently nil.[9] He recommends patients in search of rejuvenation to take ginseng extract in association with the full range of vitamins and trace elements 'that are most likely to be missing from a civilised regime'.

Ginseng appears to be particularly valuable for women, because it contains substances known as saponins which mimic the action of the female hormone oestrogen. Tests carried out at the Royal Marsden Hospital, London have shown that ginseng, when taken by older women, can cause breast enlargement and an increase in sexual responsiveness. Similar trials, carried out at Turku University, Finland, suggest that menopausal women may find ginseng sexually stimulating because it leads to a moistening of the vagina.[10]

Damiana is the other herb with a proven track record as an aphrodisiac. This was first used as a sex stimulant by the Aztecs of Mexico over 500 years ago. Years later it became the active ingredient of many Victorian nostrums for sexual debility, such as 'Damaroids' and 'Stifferine', the nerve invigorator offered to men who found it difficult to gain or sustain an erection. These nerve invigorators promised to 'make old men young again', and were sold with pictures of elderly men holding aloft a bouncing baby while their young wives looked on with obvious admiration of their potency.

Britain's leading textbook of herbal medicine supports these claims. Damiana, it reports, is an aphrodisiac which has a direct action on the reproductive organs.[11] This is how it gained its official, botanical name *Turnera aphrodisiaca*.

This combination of vitamins, essential trace minerals, anti-oxidants, ginseng and damiana would appear to be a safe and sensible food supplement for anyone keen to increase their sex drive. It is now available in Britain under the trade name Aphrogen (see page 210).

Sexercise 17
Dr Lake's Sensuous Salad

By and large the finest sources of vitamins, minerals and natural anti-oxidants are fruit and vegetables. These raw foods can also be used to form the basis of an erotically tempting salad. This recipe was provided by Dr Max Lake, a distinguished Australian surgeon who is also one of the world's leading authorities on sex attractant pheromones.

In his book *Scents and Sensuality* he explains that certain raw foods 'hint of sexual pleasure, either at the time of eating or several hours later when they have been absorbed and appear in the body odour'.[12] Some achieve this effect by mimicking the pheromone androsterone. The salad foods which generate this come-hither perfume are parsley, celery (both stem and leaves), young parsnips (sliced into fine strips), celeriac, carrot tops (finely chopped) and, if you can get them, bean sprouts, which contain an aromatic substance closely akin to the human pheromone isobutyraldehyde.

To prepare a sensuous salad mix these ingredients together in a salad bowl with French dressing, a touch of garlic and a sprinkling of nutmeg. Don't overdo the garlic, or you'll risk repelling your partner, and don't be over-generous with the nutmeg or you'll get a 'high' you don't expect. (The drug Ecstasy is a member of the amphetamine family and was first derived from nutmegs in 1919.)

This salad should be taken two or three hours before a special date. But be prepared for the consequences. Take heed of the warning issued by an earlier writer on sexual arousal: 'Our conscience obliges us to warn shy people of the aphrodisiac property of celery that they might abstain from eating it, or at least use it prudently. It is enough to stress that it is not in any way a salad for bachelors.'

SUMMARY
- Avoid taking medically prescribed drugs which can reduce your libido, especially sedatives, tranquillisers, anti-depressants, oestrogen and many anti-hypertensives.
- Keep your consumption of alcohol within reasonable limits. A little of what you fancy does you good, by releasing your inhibitions, but you'll discover that too much 'increases the desire but takes away the performance'.
- Make sure you're eating a well-balanced diet rich in vitamins and minerals, for loss of libido can sometimes be associated with mild levels of malnutrition.
- If you think your diet may be poor, consider taking food supplements containing a broad spectrum of vitamins and minerals (especially zinc, iron and vitamin B) and the three major anti-oxidants, beta-carotene, vitamin C and vitamin E.
- Ginseng and damiana are the herbs with the greatest claims to having aphrodisiac powers. These can be obtained from most health food stores.
- Eating salad foods can increase your allure by boosting your output of sex attractant pheromones, according to Australian expert Dr Max Lake. This is especially true of salads which include parsley, celery, young parsnips, celeriac, carrot tops and bean sprouts.

Seventeen

Tea for Two

Casualty doctors have little alternative but to treat their patients as 'cases' – a fractured pelvis, punctured lung or cardiac arrest. But the same impersonal approach can't be used when dealing with sexual problems, which can rarely be treated effectively out of their mental, emotional and social context. A man may find it difficult to get an erection with his wife, but may become horny the moment he meets his girlfriend. In the same way a woman may be a chilly sheila with her husband, but a flaming Phyllis with her partner at the tennis club. In these instances lack of sex drive arises, not from the physical disorders of an *individual*, but from the psychosocial problems of a *relationship*.

Many people have argued in favour of 'free love', but no loving relationship is totally free of social ties and emotional responsibilities. It's said that the most important thing in life is to find someone to love. The second most important thing is to have someone who loves you. The third is to have the first two happening together.

There is no doubt that sexual vitality and drive are strengthened by a healthy, harmonious relationship. The two ingredients – healthy sex and harmonious coupling – go together. They form part of a closed, feedback loop in which sexual satisfaction leads to a happy relationship, and a happy relationship to greater sexual satisfaction.

You Were Meant for Me

One of the loveliest of all the ancient allegories is the myth of the androgyne, the primordial creature born of the moon which was sliced into two by Zeus. One half was man, the other half woman. Throughout time the creature existed in this divided state, but each part was constantly yearning to be reunited with its androgynous twin. This romantic legend exists in slightly different forms in most of the major cultures of the world.[1]

In our public lives the sexes are sharply divided. The word sex derives from the Latin *sexus* meaning a section or split. This schism sometimes persists into our intimate relationships, when sex becomes no more than the solitary performances of two consenting adults. But at its best love becomes a spiritual union, an androgynous fusion when two people become 'one flesh'.

When we come together in the sexual act we achieve a symbolic union of the universal male and female principles. For that brief while, the yin and yang of the Chinese philosophers become merged, and we achieve existential wholeness. Many people find this a deeply satisfying experience, as Rollo May testifies in his book *Love and Will*: 'The moment of greatest significance in love-making, as judged by what people remember in the experience and what patients dream about, is not the moment of orgasm. It is rather the moment of entrance, the moment of penetration.'[2]

Men are often accused of using sex only as a means of physical release, but when Shere Hite asked her vast sample of men: 'Why do you like intercourse?' only 3 per cent mentioned the pleasure of orgasm in their replies. Generally the responses highlighted the joy and warmth of the physical intimacy. A typical response was: 'Even more important than the orgasm is being able to wrap your arms and legs and whatever else around another human being. It makes you feel less alone, more alive.'[3] When we make love in this way we do so not to fertilise an egg, but to fertilise a relationship.

Somebody Loves Me

Alienation is said to be the great psychological sickness of our age. We are born alone, we live alone and we die alone. This is one of our generation's favourite shibboleths, which is in fact a gross and depressing distortion of the truth. Our lives begin, not in isolation, but at the moment of fertilisation when male and female cells unite and start the miraculous process of birth. Thereafter, far from being alone, most of our richest experiences come from the close relationships we establish between mother and infant, parent and child and husband and wife. The deeper and closer these relationships grow, the richer and more vibrant they become.

The great criticism of promiscuity is not that it is immoral, but that it distracts time and energy from the vital task of building a single, all-absorbing sexual union. You can't have teachers without pupils, and equally well you can't expect to find a dynamic Romeo without a sexually exciting Juliet.

Sex drive is far more than the random overflow of libidinous energy, as Freud envisaged. It is also a direct response to our social and emotional situation. As such it is open to environmental manipulation. If you have a stimulating partner you vastly increase your chances of feeling exuberantly sexy. If, on the other hand, you and your partner are ill-matched – antagonistic or uncongenial – your relationship is unlikely to be blessed with erotic vitality.

Marie Stopes knew a thing or two about love, even though she had some very strange ideas about sexual physiology. She recognised that we all have a deep-felt need to find a mate. To describe this intimate and lasting bonding, she revived the very beautiful old English word 'duity'. This defines a state of human togetherness not far removed from the cosmic unity which is the goal of metaphysical and mystical experience.[4] I find this word delightfully evocative, and will use it throughout the remainder of this book, even though it no longer appears in standard English dictionaries.

Eliminate the Negative

A relationship which nourishes sexual passion can be developed by fostering within it those behaviours which fan the flames of love, and shunning those which quench its fires. To adopt this programme of marriage enrichment 'you've got to accentuate the positive, eliminate the negative'. This can be done by observing the following Ten Commandments, the first five of which are 'dos' and the next five 'don'ts'.

The First Commandment
Thou shalt not subject your partner to unnecessary aggravation
Many relationships founder because they cannot withstand the onslaught of constant argument. How can you feel loving towards a person who's just bawled you out for denting the bumper of the car? Many women get into the habit of constantly criticising their husbands for their petty indiscretions and then wonder why they're not the most attentive of lovers. 'Stop kicking against the pricks', was Marie Stopes' delightfully innocent advice to nagging wives. Dr Helen Kaplan agrees that this constant carping is a contributory cause of erotopenia. 'Anger evoked by silly squabbles, petty annoyances and simple irritations can "turn off" sexual feelings,' she wrote.[5]

In practice it is the soft answer which turns away wrath, whereas an aggressive response only provokes further anger. When Sir Isaac Newton propounded his Third Law of Motion – 'To every action there is always an equal and opposite reaction' – he was at the same time providing a sound, if unintentional, commentary on human behaviour. As ye sow, so shall ye reap. Spread criticism and you will reap criticism. Give love and you will receive love.

It's also a good rule to observe the ancient dictum 'Never let the sun go down on your wrath.' Make sure that every day ends with a kiss and a cuddle.

The Second Commandment
Thou shalt not make unreasonable sexual demands upon your partner

It's one of the eternal mysteries of life that we often choose to spend our lives with someone whose tastes are very different from our own. If they like to go to bed early, we prefer to stay up late. If they dig rock and roll music, we probably rave about the quieter strains of Handel and Bach. If they're fresh-air fiends, we invariably prefer to live in a fug with windows closed and fires blazing. In a good relationship it's generally possible to adapt to these clashes of interest. But it's not so easy to cope when you're a sex fiend and your androgynous twin opts to take a vow of lifelong celibacy. This mismatch, known as desire incongruity, is an exceedingly common cause of marital distress.

Two American marital therapists, Ellen Frank and Carol Anderson, carried out a detailed study of a hundred happily married couples. Their aim was to find the ingredients of a successful relationship. Marital satisfaction, they discovered, was not related to the number of times the couples made love. Some *never* had intercourse, others had it twice a month or two or three times a week. What mattered was that both partners found that the frequency closely matched their ideal. 'The crucial issue for marital satisfaction is the ability to work out a pattern acceptable to both partners,' the researchers concluded.[6]

Within a successful duity, it should be possible to cope with the problems caused by desire incongruity. The least amorous partners can enhance their sex drive by following the sexercises in this book. If they are too tired to have intercourse they can express their love for their partners in ways which are equally demonstrative but less physically demanding. On other occasions they may recognise the urgency of their mates' need and bring them to orgasm manually or by oral stimulation. Meanwhile the sexier members of a duo can play their part by showing greater consideration for their mates, perhaps by choosing an occasion for love-making when they are less tired, or by devoting more time to the process of sexual arousal. (Couples can get a better understanding of

155

any differences in the strength of their individual sex drives by completing the questionnaire on page 208.)

Desire incongruence is undoubtedly a problem, but not an insoluble one. As Helen Kaplan writes: 'A couple can learn to accommodate with sensitivity and love to an imbalance in sexual appetite, as loving couples do with imbalances in other spheres of life.'[7]

Sexual disappointments are easier to tolerate when all other aspects of a relationship are harmonious. This was discovered by two psychologists who found that a good predictor of marital satisfaction was obtained by subtracting the number of rows a couple had from the number of times they had sexual intercourse.[8]

The Third Commandment
Thou shalt not use love for selfish ends
Sex flourishes in a relationship where love is given altruistically rather than for personal gain. Our partners should be ends in themselves, rather than means to an end. Our love for them should be a response to their own intrinsic worth and not conditional on their willingness to iron our shirts, boost our ego, keep us in the lap of luxury or meet our sexual needs.

This is one of the true tests of emotional maturity. The mature individual treats sex as a natural expression of love; the immature person as a way of compensating for their personal inadequacies. To the lonely, it offers a temporary way of overcoming their sense of isolation. To the weak, it provides a fleeting illusion of dominance and power. To the emotionally inadequate, it presents transient proof that they are lovable.

But the love which awakens and *sustains* the passions of others is neither end-gaining nor selfish. In the words of St Bernard: 'Love seeks no cause beyond itself, and no limit; it is its own fruit, its own enjoyment. I love because I love; I love in order that I may love.'

The Fourth Commandment
Thou shalt not shackle your relationships with the burden of unreasonable expectations
One of the great problems with modern marriage is that we believe that there should be no problems with modern marriage. We live in a fantasy world in which we get wed and live happily ever after – no troubles, no tears, no temper tantrums. But intimate relationships rarely run this smoothly, and certainly not in their early days.

At one time women married to raise a family and achieve a reasonable degree of material security. These are goals which 90 per cent of women can attain. Then they demanded sexual and orgasmic satisfaction, something which at present only 70 per cent of women accomplish, so the number of dissatisfied wives trebled. More recently women have been taught to aim their sights at multiple orgasms, a feat which fewer still attain. Now the quest is for mutual orgasms, wall-to-wall romance, total freedom, non-stop togetherness and perfect understanding; a list of Utopian wants which is granted only to those who live in the never-never world of fantasy fiction.

The more unrealistic our demands, the greater our potential for disappointment. The secret of success in love, as in every other walk of life, is to make a bouquet of the flowers within your grasp.

The only time you should put your partner on a pedestal is when you want him or her to paint the ceiling.

The Fifth Commandment

Thou shalt not criticise the mote which is in your partner's eye before you have cast out the beam which lies within your own

Love feeds on praise and withers when it is subjected to constant censure and reproach. When we first meet, we see only each other's attributes. When the first heady flush of romance is over we suddenly develop 20:20 vision, but only for each other's faults. At the outset love is blind; later it needs to become a trifle short-sighted.

Too many couples, instead of building each other up, spend their lives trying to cut each other down to size. They become perpetual Darby and Groans, never satisfied with their partner's performance. One city businessman was constantly complaining about his wife's extravagance. 'If only you could prepare a decent meal we could sack the cook,' he moaned. To which his wife replied: 'If only you knew how to satisfy me in bed, we could sack the gardener.' Comments like these show a total ignorance of human psychology. When it comes to behavioural training we respond to the carrot, but invariably rebel against the stick. If the executive in the story had really wanted to dispense with the services of a cook he should have *praised* his wife's culinary skills. Then she would have spent more time in the kitchen and made the help of a cook superfluous. In the same way, if only she'd made a fuss of his skills as a Don Juan, he'd have become a far more attentive lover, leaving the gardener to perform on the beds outside the house.

'Seek and ye shall find' is a truism which applies to human relationships. If you look for love, you will find love. If you monitor your mate's behaviour for signs of indifference, coldness, hatred and spite you'll find signs of all four every day you spend together.

Accentuate the Positive

Many people wonder how to mend a broken marriage, but most broken marriages were never whole to begin with. They were built on the shifting sand of sexual attraction, without the binding mortar of love and understanding which are exemplified in the next five commandments.

The Sixth Commandment
Thou shalt strengthen thy relationship by building bridges rather than defensive walls
Man is the only animal that regularly mates face to face. In doing so we expose our vulnerable parts, belly, chest and throat. We also establish eye-to-eye contact and throw open the windows of our souls to mutual scrutiny. Many people shrink from this intimacy and vulnerability and seek to protect themselves behind an emotional carapace. This shelters them from pain, but also screens them from pleasure.

How can you have a fulfilling *relation*ship when the two partners do not relate – physically, mentally or emotionally? The greatest complaint that patients make about their doctors is their lack of openness and failure to communicate. Exactly the same is true of a high percentage of marriages. In fact, quite often it seems that couples censor their messages, or transmit them in coded form, because they don't want each other to know their innermost thoughts, wishes and needs.

We're not mind-readers. How can your partner know that you like your toes sucked, or your hair stroked, unless you tell him or her? Jill is offended because Jack comes home from an exhausting day at work and doesn't immediately compliment her on her stunning new hairstyle. She's setting him up. She wants to show that she's married to an uncaring, unobservant brute who wouldn't notice even if she'd had a face lift or was dressed as a cowboy. Otherwise, if she'd really wanted the compliment, she could have been more direct in her approach and asked outright: 'Darling, how do you like my new hairstyle?'

And what about the mixed messages we send to one another? The occasions when we say one thing and mean something totally different. Even marriage guidance counsellors are guilty of this offence. One recalls a typical example in the early days of her own marriage. They were desperately short of cash and, with a wedding anniversary approaching, she said to her husband: 'Let's not get each other anything for this anniversary.' Unfortunately, he took her at her word. When the great day arrived she gave him a simple present and a card, but received nothing in return –

no flowers, no cards, no gift. She was bitterly disappointed and cried for days. He was nonplussed. 'But you said we shouldn't get each other anything!' he protested. That indeed was what she'd *said*, but it was in no way what she'd *meant*. What she should have said, as she realised later, was: 'Since we don't have a lot of money, let's just get each other a small token of our love. It doesn't have to be expensive. It really means a lot to me to get a card and something I know is from your heart.'[9]

For marriages to succeed, we've got to open up the channels of honest communication. Above all we need to talk. At the start of relationships today it's often still the male who does the majority of the talking, as he tries to woo and win his sweetheart. But once she's caught in the tender trap he often becomes as taciturn as a Trappist monk. From then onwards it's generally the wife who does the bulk of the talking. If she's lucky, and poses some direct questions, she may get a few grunts, or monosyllabic acknowledgements in response. This is, and always has been, a common cause of marital friction. Socrates drew attention to the problem when he asked his fellow Athenians: 'Are there any people with whom you have less conversation than with your wife?' Men treat their wives as strangers by day, and then expect them to act as intimates by night. This rarely works.

We need to devote more time to conversation, which is a vital part of sexual foreplay and should be made an equally essential part of sexual afterplay. (The word 'converse' was at one time a synonym for sexual intercourse.) A start can be made by sharing confidences. If a wife tells her husband about her first love affair, or the fantasies she had as a young girl when she started to masturbate, the probability is that he will reciprocate and tell her about *his* early sexual experiences. Soon they will be sharing their innermost feelings, thoughts and needs, and discovering things about each other that they never knew before. Many women know far more about their partner's choice of TV programme than about their sexual preferences. And many men are woefully ignorant of their wives' pet hates and loves. If you think this doesn't apply to you, try the following quiz:

How Well Do You Know Your Lover?
1. When, and with whom, did she have her first love affair?
2. Are there any skeletons in his family cupboard? (Financial or moral scandals, such as prison sentences, bankruptcies, illegitimate children, mistresses.)
3. What does she consider to be the thing you most commonly argue about?

4. Does he have any scars or vaccination marks on his body, and if so where?
5. What is the size of her shoe and dress size?
6. Does he have sexual fantasies, and if so, what are they most likely to be about?
7. Did he collect anything, such as stamps, foreign coins or matchbox labels, when he was young?
8. Did she ever read a pornographic book or watch a blue movie, and if so, did it turn her on?
9. What book is he reading at the moment?
10. What ambition is she most anxious to achieve?
11. Has he any special fears – of heights, spiders or public speaking – which he tries to hide?
12. If you had an anniversary to celebrate, and you wanted to give her an inexpensive treat, what would give her greatest pleasure?
13. What was he wearing last time you went out for an evening together?
14. What is the achievement of which he is most proud?
15. Who does she most admire and would most like to emulate?

SCORING
Over 12   Remarkable.
10–12   Good, but could be more observant.
7–9   Fair. Needs to take more interest.
Under 7   Poor. Communication sadly lacking.

Improve your social communication, and you'll automatically increase the richness and intimacy of your sexual relationship.

The Seventh Commandment
Thou shalt share all you have with your partner, including money, position and power
To be successful, a marriage needs to be a union of equals, not a constant power struggle, where one has the power and the other the struggle. As a patient who had just celebrated fifty happy years of marriage told me recently: 'As long as we're playing a pretty tune we don't mind who's holding the fiddle.'

Share the power, share the workload, and share the distribution of honours. Read books together. Go shopping together. Discuss the day's news together over breakfast. (Before marriage a man says he will lay down his life for his fiancée. Once they're married he won't even lay down his morning newspaper for her.) Exercise together. Eat together. Take baths together. One couple built a sauna in their house, hoping that it would ease the husband's tension aches and pains. But its most dramatic effect was stimulating rather than relaxing, as the wife reported in a letter to *Forum* magazine. 'One night, we both decided to take a sauna together. On entering, our thoughts were on anything but sex. But soon we discovered that the intense, dry heat had an aphrodisiac effect on both of us. Making love that night inside the sauna was more exciting than any other night of our ten years of marriage.'[10]

Exciting things happen to people who share their everyday lives. And the more intimate the shared experience, the greater the aphrodisiac effect. But when you open up the revelatory floodgates do so gradually or you may get swamped. Don't make the mistake that Tolstoy did. At the ripe age of thirty-four he married Sonya, the eighteen-year-old daughter of the Kremlin's resident physician. Wanting to lay bare his soul, he immediately told her about the sexual exploits in his adventurous, murky past. He showed her his secret diaries, which carried accounts of his previous love affairs, including one homosexual liaison. The poor girl was devastated. Too much had been shared, too soon; which is probably worse than sharing too little too late.

There is a place for secrecy in marriage, providing it serves a protective function; but there is no place for indifference and neglect.

The Eighth Commandment
Thou shalt accept your partner for what they are, not for what you hope they will become
Nobody is perfect, and certainly not to one's closest confidants and friends. We marry our partners for their good points, then spend the rest of our lives blaming them for their bad points. It's rather like buying a country cottage. We see it first on a summer's day, and love it for its thatched roof, inglenook fireplace and wistaria-covered porch. We take up residence, and two years later we notice only the snags; the leaking roof, the draughts, the rattling window frames and the noise from the passing jets. These defects were there before, but we didn't notice them. We saw only the old-world charms, the fireplace, flowers and thatch, and these remain, even though familiarity may have veiled them from our sight. So it is with our close and lasting relationships. We see the warts, but fail to notice the beauty spots.

We spend our time wanting to change people, rather than enjoy them.

We often worry whether our partners love us for the 'right' reasons. But providing we're engaged on the healing task of filling the world with love and affection, can there really be any 'wrong' reasons?

One highly successful businessman was secretly troubled that he was wanted only for his wealth and asked his young wife: 'Darling, would you still love me if I lost my job and you had to give up the chauffeur-driven car, and we couldn't afford the house and the private jet and I had to cancel your dress allowance and credit cards?'

'Of course I'd still love you,' she replied. 'But I'd miss you.'

The Ninth Commandment

Thou shalt give thy partner the freedom to grow and to express his or her own personality

Life means growth, and there can be no growth in personality when individuals lack autonomy and are denied the liberty to express their own feelings and pursue their own goals. It is only when two such autonomous, but interdependent, individuals meet that we see a power-ful duity formed. All other unions, since they are between immature partners, must fall short of their full potential. The nearest analogy in the natural world is the fusion of two distinct chemical compounds, which can exist as fully functional entities in their own right – like glycerine and nitric acid – but are far more powerful when combined. In this case the end result of the combination is nothing short of dynamite (given one or two other preconditions which poetic licence permits an author, and, I hope, all but the most pedantic reader, to overlook.) This fusion of elements was recognised by Carl Jung, who wrote: 'The meeting of two personalities is like the contact of two chemical substances; if there is any reaction, both are transformed.' That's when the power is generated and the sparks fly.

The Tenth Commandment

Thou shalt seek at all times to meet thy partner's needs

We marry partly to meet certain inherent needs. Chief of these are the need for security, the need for companionship, the desire for physical intimacy, mutual support and self-esteem and the longing to love and be loved. The more these needs are met within the union, the more satisfactory and secure the duity becomes. Why go out for a hamburger when you're being offered peppered fillet steak at home? After all, we're not so very far removed from our primate cousins, and as Leonard Williams, who for many years has kept a colony of South American woolly monkeys on the Cornish coast, observes: 'No animal wants to escape if the area it inhabits satisfies its material and psychological needs.'[11]

For years we've emphasised the battle between the sexes. This has become the stuff of folklore and the substance of endless popular jokes. But the successful partnership is built on mutual support, not on internecine rivalry and strife. This was stressed by St Augustine, who deduced from the Genesis myth that: 'If God had meant woman to rule over man, He would have taken her out of Adam's head. Had he destined her to be his slave, from his feet. But God took woman out of the man's side, for He made her to be an helpmate and an equal to him.'

Sexercise 18
Tokens of Affection

Behavioural psychologists have shown that it *is* possible to modify long-standing behaviour patterns, providing we use adequate positive and negative 'reinforcers', which, in everyday language, means by operating an appropriate system of punishments and rewards. Unfortunately, within marriages, as within the field of industrial management, it's always been more popular to wield the punitive stick than to offer the encouraging carrot, but it rarely works as well, as workers at the Behaviour Exchange Clinic in Denton, Texas demonstrated in the early 1970s.

They took a series of unhappily married couples, many of whom had been nagging each other for years, and encouraged them to praise the good behaviour of their partners rather than criticise the bad. The technique they used was to distribute a handful of plastic tokens, which were to be given out as rewards whenever their partners gave them pleasure. One man gave his wife a token whenever she let him kiss her, two when she permitted heavy petting and three when she allowed sexual intercourse. The technique seems blatant and crude, but within two months their coital rate soared from two or three times a year to five times a week. The staff at the Denton Clinic found that even when the distribution of tokens was stopped 'the new behaviour continued to the general satisfaction of the once unhappy couple'.[12]

We all need recognition and praise, and the bestowal of tokens seems to be one way of showing this appreciation. To use this technique, equip yourself with a supply of plastic tokens. (Counters from a toy shop are excellent, but you could make do with champagne corks – after you've enjoyed the contents of the bottles!) Then hand them out whenever your partner gives you an unexpected pleasure – cooks a special meal, writes you a love letter or phones you during the day, simply to say 'I love you.'

Then, when your partner has collected twelve tokens, the agreement should be that you will take him or her out for a celebratory meal. That way everyone will be happy – you, your partner and the restaurateur. I'm sure the technique will work, but would be grateful for some feedback. So do please let me know how you fare.

We've Lost That Loving Feeling

By using these enrichment techniques you can build a closely integrated duity, full of fun and warmth, in which affection flourishes and sexual love abounds. But you may still have to face the problem of boredom, when 'the first, fine, careless rapture' of the relationship wears off. This is an exceedingly common cause of marital breakdown and an equally widespread cause of sexual apathy.

Matrimony is a great institution, but who wants to be married to an institution? Love grows stale if it isn't adequately nourished, and it is this monotony which, according to Masters and Johnson, 'is probably the most constant factor in the loss of the ageing male's interest in sexual performance with his partner.'[13]

This ennui occurs in other animals. If a male and female rat are placed together in a cage they invariably copulate. But once the honeymoon period is over the rate of sexual activity declines. If the female rat is taken out of the cage and replaced by another, the male immediately regains his sexual urge and copulates at the same high rate as before. A similar effect is seen in Macaque monkeys, which quickly become bored with a steady partner, but regain their erotic drive, increasing their sexual activity fifteen-fold, when they are introduced to an exciting new 'mistress'.[14] This phenomenon – the link between libido and novelty – is known to biologists as the Columbus Factor.

You Make Me Feel so Young

One obvious solution to sexual boredom is to take a lover. This age-old remedy for sexual boredom has been widely used. In the Polynesian islands it was traditional for elderly men to take a young concubine when they found their sexual powers waning. When this practice was frowned upon by Western missionaries they complained that they were being deprived too soon of their potency. According to one anthropologist: 'Older men often comment today that without young women to excite them and without the variety once provided by changing concubines, they have become sexually inactive long before their time. To them a wife is sexually exciting only for a few years after marriage.'[15]

Women are often the major victims of marital boredom, either as cuckolded lovers or dissatisfied wives. It's said that Calvin Coolidge, the US President, was not as attentive to his wife as she would have liked. One day when they were on a visit to a poultry farm she was told that the rooster often performed his services eight or nine times a night. 'Please see to it that the President is given that information,' she instructed her guide. The President was duly told and after a moment's thought asked: 'Same chicken each time?' On being told the coupling was always with different birds the President countered: 'Then see that Mrs Coolidge is given *that* information!'

You're Getting to be a Habit with Me

The Columbus Factor is now a far more insidious threat to marital stability than ever before. In the eighteenth century the average age for marriage was twenty-eight and the average life expectancy thirty-two. So the vast majority of marriages didn't have time to experience the seven-year itch. Second marriages were common in those days, but they were caused by death rather than divorce. Now we have marriages lasting fifty or more years. How can we keep them fresh? How can we avoid the contempt which is born of familiarity?

One way, often recommended by marriage counsellors, is to recapture the spontaneity that enlivens most relationships in their early days. To act on impulse rather than by rote. One counsellor was advising a couple whose main complaint was that their sex life had become infinitely boring. Every night they followed the same routine, he came home from work, read the evening paper, they ate supper, watched two hours of television and at eleven o'clock sharp they retired to bed, by which time they were too flat to have fun. 'No wonder,' the sex therapist said. 'You've done the unforgivable thing of making sex boring. You've got to stop following a set routine. Be impulsive. Don't wait until eleven o'clock each night. Have sex whenever the urge takes you.' They promised to follow his advice and returned the following week, their faces wreathed in smiles. 'Did it work?' the counsellor asked.

'Splendidly!' the wife replied. 'The very next night we were sitting down to a meal of spaghetti Bolognese, and after a couple of glasses of wine, Dave started kissing me, fondling me and then he tore off my bra. A few seconds later I was stark naked on the floor. The sex was more exciting than we've had for years. The only trouble is that we've now been banned for life from Luigi's Pasta House.'

You Never Did it Like That

Boredom encourages people to experiment outside marriage; but a far simpler solution is to experiment *inside* marriage. Marriage is a long vacation, on which the travel brochures can be more exciting than the trip, unless the holiday is made exciting and varied. When Madame de Pompadour asked her doctor's advice about keeping Louis XV happy, he replied: 'Change is the greatest aphrodisiac of all.' If wives are bored and looking for outside excitement, it's almost certainly because their husbands are boring company: always doing the same things, in the same place and in the same boring way. As Balzac said: 'If a man cannot afford distinct and different pleasures to the woman he has made his wife on two successive nights, he has married too soon.'

The Way We Were

Variety is the spice of married life: boredom the kiss of death. Too much sameness leads to a state of holy deadlock. If you dreamed of candlelit dinners for two, strolling hand in hand along a moonlit beach, holding hands in the theatre or escaping for an unscheduled weekend in the country, what's stopping you realising your dreams? If you find your present lifestyle is boring, change it. Follow the advice that Ellen Kreidman gives the women attending her marriage enrichment classes: 'Do something unpredictable, spontaneous, and different. Don't worry that you're "not the type" – everyone has the ability to be creative and exciting. It just takes time, energy, and the willingness to try something different.'[16]

And there's no need to indulge in bizarre sexual behaviour. Kinky sex soon becomes every bit as boring as straight sex if it's endlessly repeated. Couples should try everything once, providing it's not incest or caber-tossing.

Sexercise 19
Russian Roulette

Dare to be different! Buy a large pack of postcards and write on each one the instructions for a novel activity that you think will add spice to your relationship. Be as inventive as you can and try to choose events that you think will both please and excite your mate. The more playful the activities the better. When I was in the RAF the book which was taken out most frequently from our station library was called *Fun in Bed*. It was a book about occupational therapy, disappointingly, but its popularity showed that there is a real demand for more playful sexual relationships.

Shuffle the cards, then pick one at random and follow the directions. If you're stumped for ideas here are a few suggestions:

- Scatter 'I love you' hearts around the home where you know your partner will find them.
- Have an evening out doing something you've never done before – bingo, dog racing or ice-skating. One couple were escaping from their blazing home and when they got to the front door the husband noticed that his wife was laughing. 'What on earth have you got to laugh about?' he asked.

  'I can't help it,' she said. 'This is the first time we've gone out together for five years.'
- Arrange an excuse to meet your partner wearing nothing under your top coat. The nightclub singer Fernanda de Castro put on a voluptuous mink coat to say goodbye to Duke Ellington when he was departing from Las Vegas station. Just as the train was about to leave she opened the coat. Underneath she was bare; and the delighted Duke found himself wrapped in both her body and the coat as he received a passionate farewell kiss. The ploy worked for Fernanda, why not for you?
- Give your partner a present, not necessarily an expensive one, but something he's never had before.
- Send your lover a note, when she is at a meeting or large public gathering, telling her that you find her incredibly sexy and you can't wait to get her home and into bed. Sir John Mills, when celebrating nearly fifty-two years of marriage to his wife Mary, said: 'You have to work at a marriage. You have to keep it fresh.' When he's at a public dinner, and separated from Mary, he likes to send her a note saying: 'Do you remember me? I love you.' 'That way the thing doesn't become ordinary,' he says.

- Give your partner a top-to-toe soap in the bath, or a nude body massage.
- Try making love in a different position. Maybe, for a change, try the rear-entry position. (This was banned by the church, not, as many believe, because it aped the copulation of animals, but because the holy fathers feared that it was too pleasurable!) Tallulah Bankhead is said to have tried a variety of coital positions: the normal one made her feel claustrophobic and the others she complained gave her either a stiff neck or lockjaw.
- Play a sexy game, like strip poker or noughts and crosses using body paint on bare skin. Or take your partner on a naked wheelbarrow race around the house or challenge him to a nude leapfrog race in the bedroom. (But remember the notice in the nudist club, posted at the time of the annual sports gala: 'Everyone who takes part in the leapfrog race must complete all jumps.')
- Take your partner by surprise by showing her affection in public when she least expects it. This will disarm her and at the same time help to increase her self-esteem. One housewife, bored and depressed by her humdrum marriage, went with her husband to a psychiatrist for counselling. After a few minutes the therapist threw his arms around her neck and gave her a long, tender kiss. She perked up immediately and became positively effervescent. 'See', the counsellor said to her husband, 'that's all your wife needs and I want her to have it every Monday, Wednesday and Friday.' 'If you say so,' the husband replied, 'but there's one snag. I can bring her every Monday and Wednesday, but on Friday I play bridge.'
- Make love in a location you've never tried before. Be bold. Don't wait until you're in bed. Try it in the garden, in front of the fire, while you're out on a country walk or while you're babysitting for friends. President Kennedy did it in a cupboard; Josephine Baker on a train; Gary Cooper on the beach; Mussolini on a staircase and the lesbian writer Natalie Barney in a theatre box. Experiment. Dare to be different.

  One sex counsellor interviewed 300 couples in depth and found that many of them were in a rut and longed to do something adventurous. 'Would you believe that a surprising number of middle-aged couples with comfortable homes and beds think it's the height of erotic stimulation to make love on the back seat of a car?' (If you try this particular location do take care – several backs have been injured in this way and ended up on my treatment couch!)

- Try the Crimean Tartar's method. This is a test of mind over matter which requires the aid of a kitchen timer. Wind the clock and set the alarm to ring after thirty minutes. During this time you and your partner must lie naked together, in a position of full penetration, without reaching a climax. For that half-hour you can kiss, pet and fondle, but you must otherwise lie still without moving your pelvis or attempting to reach an orgasm. This practice is very similar to *carezza*, the age-old method of birth control or *coitus-reservatus*, with one delightful difference: when the alarm rings you don't separate, but proceed to a climax which is often all the more intense because of the prolonged period of arousal and enforced self-control.
- Re-enact a love scene from your favourite movie. Or, if you prefer it, imagine that you have been engaged to take part in a blue movie and are putting on a simulated sex show which will have the audience squirming in their seats. (Do this with conviction, and you'll soon find that you're not simulating, but acting for real.)
- Equip yourself with some coloured paper and challenge your partner to a korigami contest. This is a branch of the ancient Japanese art of origami in which the participants fold paper to create colourful paper ornaments to adorn the penis.
- Buy your mate some specially sexy underwear. Why is it that we only buy fresh undies when we're visiting the doctor or embarking on a new affair? Couldn't we wear something fetching to excite our long-term lovers? Is it any surprise that a man comes home late from the office when he knows that his wife will be wearing curlers and an old, threadbare cardigan? The surprise to me is that he comes home at all.
- Agree for once to take the dominant role. If you're the female of the partnership take the top berth. That way you won't notice that the ceiling needs painting. And if you're the male member of the partnership, when was the last time you were so eager to make love that you had to help her out of clothes? Jules and Jane had been married long enough to have sunk into a deep, marital rut in which everything was done by numbers. But one night Jane rebelled. 'Let's have sex,' he said, when the television proved too boring to watch any more.

'No!', she replied with unusual firmness, as she pulled on her long, winceyette nightgown.

When Jules finally joined her in bed he tried again: 'Pull up your nightie, honey,' he asked. Again she gave an adamant 'No!'

At that moment the front doorbell rang and Jules went down to answer it. She seized her chance and slipped out of bed and locked the bedroom door. Her husband was furious when he returned, and banged furiously on the door. 'Let me in, let me in!' he screamed. 'If you don't unlock the door I'll break it down.'

'Listen to Mr Tough Guy,' she replied calmly. 'He talks about breaking down the door and yet he can't even lift up my nightdress.'

- Compete to make the most exotic ice-cream sundae on each other's belly – with whipped cream and chocolate sauce topping – then eat them up as an *hors d'oeuvre* to the main course.

Keep your partnership fresh by indulging in these frolics, and you'll find that life is not what it used to be when you were first together – it's better!

SUMMARY

- You and your partner will feel more loving towards one another if you avoid unnecessary squabbles and criticism.
- Your sex life will blossom if you make a conscious attempt to accentuate the positive aspects of your relationship, and at the same time try to eliminate the negative elements. One of the major ways of doing this is to praise often, and blame seldom.
- Many love affairs wither through lack of proper communication. Misunderstandings arise from ignorance. If you share with your partner your innermost feelings, thoughts and needs your level of intimacy will grow. And as you lower the defensive walls which separate you, so you'll gain the freedom to give and receive each other's passion without emotional censorship or restraint.
- A mature relationship is based on reality rather than fantasy. Love is an end in itself, rather than a means to an end. You'll find your love life far fuller and freer if you accept your mate for what he or she *is*, rather than for what you hope he or she will become. Many duiities are ruined by unreasonable expectations.
- You'll reach your full sexual potential only if you exercise your autonomy. You must maintain the right to express your sexuality in your own, unique way. In the same way your partner's erotic powers will grow only if you give him or her the freedom to express his or her own personality.

- Reward your partner whenever he or she gives you sexual pleasure – with a smile, a few words of thanks or a special treat – and he or she will be more anxious to meet your needs in the future.
- Be spontaneous, adventurous, exciting, different. Your sex drive will decline if you allow your relationship to grow stale. Variety is the spice of conjugal life; boredom the kiss of death.

Eighteen

For Every Man
There's a Woman

The single most important thing about a person is their sex. Men and women differ from the moment they are born. They vary in the way they think and act and in their inherent capabilities. 'The two sexes differ so much as to be like two distinct species,' says an eminent Oxford geneticist.[1] Virtually every biological study emphasises this diversity. Whether the test is of physical function, mental performance or emotional reactivity the sexes respond in different ways. The same applies to sexual behaviour.

Since the advent of the women's movement it has become unfashionable to draw attention to this gender dimorphism; yet it remains a biological fact which has a profound effect on the way we live and the way we love.

To Each His Own

No one can deny that social forces shape the differing lifestyles of men and women, but neither education, coercion nor state legislation can eradicate the fundamental biological differences between the sexes. (These gender differences make their first appearance in the womb, so they can hardly be attributed to cultural conditioning.) No amount of conditioning can train a pig to fly, and even if boys are made to play exclusively with dolls, are taught cookery and baby care, and dressed in frocks, they will still be fundamentally different from girls. If we are to make the most of our sexual relationships, we must recognise and harness this gender difference, rather than try to deny its very existence.

Three points need to be stated, which may raise the hackles of anyone who adopts an extreme feminist viewpoint. (I would welcome a reasoned dialogue with anyone who disagrees with these opinions, or with any of the other views raised in this book):

• There are major biological differences between the sexes which have a marked effect on the developmental potential of men and women. These can be modified, but not eliminated, by cultural conditioning.

- Contemporary society, family life and sexual relations are best served by fostering, rather than denying, these inherent, sex-linked attributes.
- Men and women who follow their biological imperatives increase their chances of achieving a happy and harmonious partnership; a symbiotic union of yin and yang in which mutual understanding grows and sexual vitality flourishes.

I Enjoy Being a Girl

Just as black seems darker when viewed against a white background, so a man's masculinity appears stronger when contrasted with a woman's femininity, as does a woman's essential femaleness when highlighted by the unmistakable masculinity of her mate. By *emphasising* the gender differences, we help our partners express and expand their sexuality. By *recognising* the differences, we increase our understanding of their feelings, behaviour and sexual problems.

Some of the variance in behaviour can be explained by employing the 'selfish gene' hypothesis, which suggests that we act in ways which maximise the chances of the perpetuation of our genes. This is a relatively simple task for men, who merely need to impregnate a large number of fertile women, preferably those who are young and nubile. For women the goal is less easy to ensure. If they are to perpetuate their genes they must find, not *any* mate, but one who is powerful and strong enough to protect and support her progeny during their formative years. She needs to find a mate who is not only physically potent, but also emotionally stable, caring, kind, responsible and loyal. Finding such a paragon takes time.

This was confirmed when researchers quizzed a group of nearly 700 young men and women about their dating experience. A quarter of the men reported that they had chosen their partners and fallen seriously in love after their fourth date. This was true of only 15 per cent of women, most of whom hadn't selected their eventual partner even after twenty dates.[2]

Women generally take longer to fall in love because, unlike men, they are more interested in sexual *relationships* than in impersonal sexual *encounters*. Most women feel that they could live without sex but not without love; whereas most men believe that they could live without love but not without sex. But the passions they feel are equally strong.

173

The Victorians created an image of ideal womanhood, pure in thought and chaste in behaviour. To believe that such a saintly creature could get pleasure from sex was a 'base slander on the fair name of womanhood'.[3] They were expected to do their duty, but not to enjoy it. While their husbands enjoyed their marital rights, they were encouraged to lie back and think of England. But numerous investigations have shown that the female sex drive, once it is freed from inhibitions and cultural restraints, is every bit as powerful as the male's. In fact, as Cornelia Otis Skinner said: 'Woman's virtue is man's greatest invention.'

Two psychologists from the University of Washington invited a group of adults to give a record of the sensations they experienced at the moment of orgasm. The reports were then given to a panel of psychologists, gynaecologists, obstetricians and medical students who were 'unable to distinguish the sex of a person from that person's description of his or her orgasm'.[4] The only exception was the account which reported that if the love-making is continued the climax recurs again and again. That *had* to be written by a woman. (Women's ability to have multiple orgasms is probably an atavistic mechanism, dating back to the days when primate females were on heat for only a limited period and during this time needed to copulate with a number of partners to maximise their chance of impregnation.)

It may still be unfashionable for women to show their sexual feelings in public, but this does not stop them expressing them on lavatory walls. During my days in the RAF I was amazed to find that the graffiti in the women's toilets were more extensive and bawdier than those in the men's. (If you wonder how I made this discovery, I can assure you there is an explanation which is innocent, if not totally believable.) Anyone who shares my intimate understanding of this subject will know that feminine graffiti is concise ('Sex kills – die happy'); wry ('Does oral sex mean just talking about it?'); profound ('A little yearning is a dangerous thing'); wise ('VD is nothing to clap about'); and imaginative ('Does the lateral coital position mean having a bit on the side?').

Women learn these literary skills at an early age, according to two psychologists from Cincinnati University who studied the graffiti in the boys' and girls' toilets in four high schools in the American mid-west and found that the girls' efforts – sexual insults, bawdy humour and obscene requests – were more than three times as numerous as the boys'.[5]

Contrary to popular belief, a high proportion of women are also turned on by pornography, blue movies and erotic novels. When a group of adults at the Institute of Stress Research, Stockholm was shown a series of erotic films, nearly all the men, and three-quarters of the women, experienced sexual arousal. Several of the women even reached a state of extreme sexual excitation, a level attained by none of the men.[6]

Man's responsibility is to help his mate release her sex drive and achieve her full erotic potential.

Miss Frigidaire

At one time women were said to suffer from 'frigidity', which made it sound as if they had a disease like chicken-pox or measles. Now it's more common to talk in terms of 'inhibited sexual desire' (ISD) which emphasises that the lack of sex drive is functional, and can probably be overcome by measures which help the individual overcome the inhibitions that prevent them from expressing their inherent sexuality.

Some doctors still treat ISD with tranquillisers, hoping that this will overcome their inhibitions in the same way as a couple of liberating Bloody Marys. But sedative drugs are often counter-productive. In high enough doses they may depress the critical faculties of the cerebrum, but at the same time they can suppress the level of arousal of the brain's sex centres, turning an inhibited but otherwise lively person into a passionless zombie.

Inhibitions are best released within the framework of a tender, patient and understanding relationship. At one time sex therapists employed surrogate partners to help their patients learn new patterns of sexual behaviour. These therapists were invariably female. I wonder why? There can have been no shortage of men able and willing to offer their therapeutic services. Can it be that they were thought incapable of showing the necessary tenderness, understanding and patience?

Fathers often took pains to see that their sons had their first sexual encounter with an experienced and understanding older woman, but they rarely took such trouble with their daughters, who were generally left to discover the facts of life at the hands of a clumsy, raw, insensitive youth.

Lack of sexual interest in a woman is invariably situational. A 'cold', passionless woman is a woman who has not yet met the man she is bound to love, said Stendhal. It is up to her partner to provide the conditions which allow her sexuality to flourish. For the chemistry to work he must not only *find* the right person, he must also *be* the right person.

175

We're Almost There

Most women can climax when they're masturbating – using their fingers, a vibrator or a rubber dildo – but approximately a third regularly fail to get an orgasm during heterosexual intercourse. Many blame their lack of responsiveness on the size or layout of their genital organs, just as a golfer blames his putter when he fails to sink a two-foot putt. Some think their vaginas are too short; others that their clitorises are too small, badly placed or excessively hooded. This is rarely the case. All but a very few women have what it takes to be orgasmic, provided it's properly used.

Most orgasms result from clitoral stimulation, and it's unfortunate that the required degree of clitoral stimulation is often more easily achieved with a finger or sex aid than with the object nature provided. The women's movement capitalised on this unsatisfactory state of affairs when they took as one of their 1960s campaign slogans: 'A woman needs a man like a fish needs a bicycle.' But while women may get sexual satisfaction through masturbation, this won't provide them with the affection and love they crave, often more urgently than they demand physical release. Most of the 3,000 American women in Shere Hite's sample said that the psychological rewards of intercourse, the closeness, love, tenderness and affection, were more important than the purely physical ones.[7] But why should a woman not enjoy both?

Mr Wonderful

If she found the right partner he could provide her with psychological love and support and also help her to achieve sexual satisfaction – *if only he knew how*. Most men are anxious to please their mates, but frequently haven't a clue what turns them on. Many would find it easier to spot a black cat in a coal cellar on a moonless night than locate their partner's clitoris. So why not take his hand and lead him on a guided tour of the promised land? Don't be shy. You'll never get what you want unless you ask for it.

It is not unusual for promiscuous women to be non-orgasmic. Often they spend their lives in a vain quest to find a macho prince to awaken their sleeping sensuality. They try an endless succession of Casanovas, toyboys, ruffians, black men, foreigners, sadists, weight-lifters, athletes and men with prodigiously sized penises, hoping that one will be able to unlock their latent sexual energy. But often they are their own jailers, for just as a fakir can make himself insensitive to pain, so a repressed woman can make herself insensitive to the pleasures of sexual arousal and fulfilment.

One woman broke through this barrier for the first time after years of unfulfilled sexual encounters. It happened one memorable night when she shed her tensions and inhibitions and enjoyed 'a real orgasm'. In the past she had sought a partner who would release her pent-up feelings. Now she discovered the reward of letting herself go. 'I never knew in all my searching and trying for orgasm,' she said, 'that it was to be found inside me and a thing of my own control.'[8]

Sexercise 20
The Kegel Exercises

Women can promote their own orgasms, not only by releasing their inhibitions, but also by making better use of their sexual apparatus.

The pelvis contains a sex organ which is little known and yet of considerable importance. Its official name is the pubococcygeus muscle (PCG for short). This is a sheet of muscle which runs in close contact with the vagina, and gives support to the pelvic organs rather like a hammock.

Strengthening this muscle is known to help women suffering from stress incontinence, who experience a leakage of urine whenever they cough or sneeze. Many women carrying out this treatment found that the exercises also enhanced their sex lives. This encouraged Dr Arnold Kegel, professor of gynaecology at the University of Southern California School of Medicine, to investigate the role of the PCG muscle in sexual intercourse. He invented a device, known as a perineometer, which could be inserted into the vagina to measure the strength of the PCG muscle. Using this gadget he measured the muscle strength of over 10,000 volunteers over a period of twenty-five years. In over 85 per cent of cases he found the muscle to be poorly developed. This weakness was associated with poor sexual performance. Conversely the women with more powerful PCG muscles – sometimes more than three times stronger – reported a higher level of sexual satisfaction.[9]

Women who develop this muscle are able to grip the penis during intercourse, rather as a milkmaid grasps and 'milks' a cow's teats. This creates a more powerful sensation for her and also for her mate. It is this control which, with practice, enables a woman to 'smoke' a cigarette held between her labial folds. (There are even reports of women who are so adept that they can insert three numbered ping-pong balls in their vaginas and then juggle them so that any one of the three can be expelled at will.)

Mercifully this degree of control is not necessary to improve sexual function. The vaginal passage itself is largely devoid of nerve endings, but not so the PCG muscle, which supports the middle third of the vagina. The stronger this muscle, and the tighter its grip on the penis, the more its sensory nerves are stimulated and the richer the flow of nerve impulses to the brain's sex centres.

To strengthen the PCG muscle, imagine that you are gripping a coin between your buttocks, or trying to check a bout of diarrhoea. Do this at odd times during the day, when you are either sitting, standing or lying. (This is probably best done in private, since one of my patients was cautioned by a policeman who noticed the rhythmic movements of her pelvis while she was waiting for a bus and thought that she was acting indecently!)

Then, having developed the muscle by regular exercise, use it to clasp the penis during intercourse. This will heighten the pleasure you both receive.

Sometimes women find it helpful when their partners take a more assertive role. There are times when they wish that they were facing a romantic Arab sheik who, instead of burying his head in a mug of cocoa, would sweep them off their feet and carry them off for a night of passion in their desert hide-away. As one of my lady patients complained: 'I don't care if there's life on another planet, I just wish there was a little more on this.'

The women's movement is urging men to develop their 'feminine' qualities of gentleness and passivity, but there are also times when they need to exercise a degree of dominance. When they are consumed with passion it is a stimulus, and also a tribute, to their partners, who gain the reassurance that they are sexually exciting and have the power to trigger off an overwhelming, primitive response in their mates. Quite understandably, one of novelist Jilly Cooper's pet hates are the men 'who fold their clothes before jumping into bed with you'.

There is a time for self-control, and also a time for complete abandon. Some women even respond to a degree of bullying, a word which strangely enough comes from the German word *buhle*, meaning lover.

Help Me Make it Through the Night

Impotence is man's main sexual problem. This is a dysfunction which is far more obvious and much more crippling than a woman's inability to climax. After all, a woman can fake an orgasm, but there is no way a man can fake an erection. In any case a woman does not need an orgasm to become pregnant, but a man cannot ensure the perpetuation of his genes unless he achieves erection, penetration and a climax. The female of the species is always potent; the male always potentially impotent.

Most men have times in their lives when the spirit is willing but the flesh is weak. These episodes may be brought on by illness, alcohol, tiredness or stress, and are generally as ephemeral as a bout of fibrositis. The penis is a wayward organ which tends to become erect on a first visit to a nudist club, when you want it to be inconspicuous, and to remain flaccid when you want it to perform. This has always been man's dilemma. As Leonardo da Vinci reported in one of his notebooks, the penis has a life of its own, 'moving sometimes of itself without licence or thought by the man, whether he is sleeping or waking, it does what it desires, and often the man is asleep and it is awake, and many times he is awake and it is asleep'.[10] Because of this, men can never feel cocksure.

Approximately 90 per cent of American men think that their penises are too small. This fear is often based on a simple optical illusion, for another man's dangling penis in a sports changing-room looks full-sized, while your own appears foreshortened when viewed from above. In any case, the length of the penis is no guide to its functional ability. Erected organs as small as half an inch have been found to give sexual satisfaction just as great as one that is a foot long (the record length for an erect penis). But this remains a matter of masculine concern, as with the man who suffered the ultimate humiliation of being arrested for indecent exposure and then let off because of insufficient evidence.

There Must Be a Way

Numerous surgical attempts have been made to improve the function of the penis. Some tribal races implant pieces of stick and bone into their penises to expand their size. A similar effect is produced by a Miami cosmetic surgeon, who injects fat into the superficial layers of the penis, a procedure he describes as 'circumferential autologous penile engorgement'. Other techniques involve injections of drugs into the blood vessels at the base of the penis, or the insertion of penile splints, which

179

have the same effect as the *os penis*, the stiffening bone which runs down the shaft of the penis of ferrets, dogs, walruses and whales.

But these heroic measures are called for only on rare occasions. Impotence is generally functional in origin rather than structural. Sometimes it comes from reading too many issues of *Cosmopolitan*, which provokes a condition known as 'performance anxiety'.

When we retire to our marital beds we promise according to our hopes but perform according to our fears. Men easily become depressed if they feel their sexual performance is deficient; if they are not giving their partners the big 'O', or are failing to meet the national 'norm' of x copulations per week. This threatens their self-esteem, which is often closely linked to their personal estimate of their potency. But coitus is only one small part of sexual behaviour, which embraces the whole range of loving encounters between partners. The average middle-aged man spends far more time shaving than copulating.

Sexercise 21
Sensate Focusing

This is a technique which aims to bring back the pleasure into sex, and remove the fear. Instead of end-gaining – fighting to achieve an erection or struggling to reach a climax – the practice demands no more than a few moments' leisurely concentration on relaxed, sensuous enjoyment. We are never less likely to achieve our goals than when we try too hard. This applies to serving at tennis, sinking a three-foot putt, or making love. A woman desperately wants to have an orgasm, and focuses her attention on this target to such an extent that she shuts herself off from the pleasurable sensations which should be reaching her brain and bringing her to the desired state of erotic arousal. A man experiences impotence once, and this transient failure upsets him so much that the next time he needs to perform he worries whether or not he will be able to get an erection. And the more he worries, the greater his problem becomes, because anxiety and fear have an inhibitory effect on his brain's sex centres.

The way to overcome this vicious circle is to set aside times for sexual encounters which specifically *exclude* any form of genital contact. During these sessions you can fondle, kiss and cuddle, but should agree to make no attempt whatsoever at sexual intercourse. By focusing on pleasure rather than performance, you'll find you not only increase your immediate enjoyment but also improve your long-term performance. Masters and Johnson discovered this

180

when they employed this technique to treat men with both primary and secondary impotence. (Primary impotence covers those cases where satisfactory erections have *never* been achieved; secondary impotence where erections were once possible but have since failed.) Both categories responded well to sensate focusing, which helped the men lose their sexual fears and recapture the simple joys of carefree loving. When the results were assessed, five years after the initial treatment, the cure rate was found to be an impressive 75 per cent for the men with secondary impotence and 60 per cent for the men with primary impotence.[11]

The important thing is to stop the endless cycle in which anxiety produces functional failure, which causes further worry, which in turn leads to worsening function. Like actors, many men think that they're only as good as their last performance. But even the world's top athletes can't always be on peak form. A sprinter wouldn't expect to record his best-ever time on the track if he was jet-lagged, exhausted and slightly drunk. So why should you, in similar circumstances, expect to give a peak performance in bed?

Listen to the wisdom of the body. If you're tired, sleep. If you're hungry, eat. If you're amorous, make love. And if you're neither of these things, just be content to hold hands on the sofa and watch a good TV play (if that isn't a contradiction in terms).

This is where it's invaluable to have an understanding mate, who reads your moods, interprets your thoughts and understands your needs.

Lady be Good

Women throughout time have known how to arouse their man. Kohl, or mascara, has been used to emphasise the fascination of the eyes since the days of Cleopatra. Lips have been reddened to make them look more sensuous and breasts made more pronounced by wearing tight sweaters, uplift bras or falsies. And the seductive walk produced by high heels or hobble skirts was in vogue long before the arrival of Marilyn Monroe. (Marilyn Monroe, as a young starlet, developed her famous sexy waddle, required for her walk-on part in a Marx Brothers' film, by removing part of the heel of one of her shoes.)

Every man has his own arousal cues. A few are foot fetishists; many more are excited by prominent behinds. This explains the appeal of tight jeans, bottom-pinching, buttock-revealing swimsuits, and the final 'bottoms-up' flourish of the can-can dance, which ethologist Desmond Morris describes as a 'version of the ancient primate rump-presentation display'.[12] Even though this is an atavistic gesture, since we rarely mount from the rear, it still acts as a powerful erotic signal for many males. (The bottom-patting which was once an acceptable courtship gesture is now considered a form of sexual harassment and so in many countries is now punishable by law.)

Yet men are sensitive creatures. They are easily sexually aroused, but they are also easily frightened by women who are too obviously and provocatively sexual. Deep down in the male subconscious is the fear that they can be damaged by powerful women. This is most clearly seen in the castration myth, which appears in different guises in most cultures. A typical example is the Maori legend of Maui, the primordial father of the human race, who tried to kill the goddess of death by entering her vagina while she slept. The onlooking birds thought this exceedingly funny, and laughed so noisily that they awoke the sleeping goddess, who saw what was happening and immediately killed Maui by crushing him between her thighs.

These latent fears can be triggered off by sexually aggressive women who provoke acute 'performance anxiety' by standing over their men like Indian snake-charmers, commanding his slumbering organ to rise. This angst was recently voiced by a man who told me: 'The trouble these days is not just that women are demanding sex more often, but that they're expecting to enjoy it.' Men have not had to face these pressures before, and one or two husbands have told me in confidence that to escape their wives' demands they have taken to going to bed early, feigning sleep or pretending to have an incapacitating back problem. Maybe these frigid excuses are the masculine equivalent of the feigned headaches and faked orgasms which women have traditionally employed to mask their own lack of sexual enthusiasm.

You Do Something to Me

Yet while men do not want their partners to be *over*-assertive, most seem keen for them to play a more active role in initiating love-making. This was discovered by researchers who questioned 200 men of all ages about their sexual preferences and found that three-quarters wanted 'more involvement by the woman before or during intercourse'. This agrees with the findings of Professor Hans Eysenck, who found that 88 per cent of male students think it right that girls should sometimes be sexually aggressive.[14] Occasionally men would like to be treated as sex objects. That would flatter their egos and boost their feelings of potency. At present many men feel under pressure to pleasure their partners. This burden would be lightened if women were ready to assume more of the responsibility for obtaining their own sexual satisfaction.

Now and again she should choose the time and place, and make the first advance. On these occasions she should determine the length of foreplay and the coital position to be adopted. On occasions she can regard the penis as a resource, a living dildo to be wielded exclusively for *her* pleasure. Some women may find this offends their sense of modesty. But such coyness can easily be overcome, because it is culturally acquired rather than genetically determined. In most modern Western societies it is normal for the man to be the dominant sexual partner. This is traditional for us; but a study of 200 other ethnic societies revealed that it is more common for the sexual initiative to be shared fairly equally between the two sexes.[15] In some the balance tips the other way, which can threaten the self-assurance of the male. This is true of the Zuni Indians, whose young women are so ribald and sexually aggressive that it is the men rather than the women who show signs of anxiety as their wedding night approaches.[16]

For men and women to achieve their full sexual potency they need the support and understanding of a caring partner. This is what makes the difference between love and lust. A young girl once explained the difference between liking and loving to writer William Faulkner. 'If I likes them I lets them,' she said. 'If I love them I helps them.'

SUMMARY

- *Vive la différence*! Men and women become more amorous when they are with a partner who shows strong sexual differentiation. Emphasise the gender differences between you – the masculinity of the male and the femininity of the female – and the thermometer will rise as the sexual chemistry starts to react.
- Don't be unduly bothered about the dimensions of your sexual organs. Breasts, penises, wombs and clitorises are infinitely varied in their size and shape – and virtually all are perfectly adequately formed to serve their preordained function.
- Women readers will probably find they can heighten their sexual pleasure, and that of their partners, by strengthening the PCG muscle which cradles their womb. This can be done by performing the Kegel exercises described in this chapter.

- If you're a victim of 'performance anxiety', and constantly worry that you're going to fail to make the grade as a sexual athlete, take a temporary break from the competitive scene. Stop striving for end results. Concentrate instead on the pleasurable 'here and now'. Follow the sensate focusing routine, and for a while be content to enjoy kissing, cuddling and fondling without proceeding to full coitus.

Nineteen

Our Love is Here to Stay

As we get older our physical performance declines. Our reflexes become slower, our stamina droops and our muscle power fails. Our sexual function shows a similar decline. This deterioration is most obvious in men, who are usually at their sexual peak in their mid-twenties. From that point onwards their potency wanes. By fifty they find it takes longer to achieve an erection. Their production of sex hormones drops, and the daily volume of semen manufactured may be twelve times less than it was in their sexual prime.

Facts like these can make depressing reading, unless you put them into context. At fifty a man is undoubtedly less capable of having repeat orgasms; but then how often in his teens did he manage to perform three times a night? As a youngster he could ejaculate much further than he can today, but is that really an essential social skill? Even at ninety he's almost certainly still fertile, providing his partner isn't at the other side of the room at the moment of climax.

We run the risk of over-emphasising the importance of these physiological changes, which need not diminish erotic interest, emotional happiness or sexual satisfaction. In fact some of the 'ageing' changes can be positively beneficial. Many women are grateful when their lovers take longer to achieve an erection, because this prolongs the period of foreplay.

As we grow older we have more time to savour the pleasures of life. Rather than bolt our meals, we can linger over them and take a gourmet's delight in each succulent mouthful. If we go for a country stroll, we may not cover the same mileage at the same breakneck speed, but we do have more time to smell the roses and enjoy the wonders of the world around us.

When we are young our attention is often focused on certain, self-appointed goals – the quest for recognition, success, self-esteem, financial security or material well-being. As we grow older these objectives become less important. We are less obsessed with reaching particular destinations and therefore have more time to enjoy the journey. We become more earthy, more in touch with the real world, more elemental. This change in outlook is well expressed by Pulitzer

Prize-winner Dr Robert Butler, founder of the National Institute of Ageing: 'Elementality – the enjoyment of the elemental things of life – may develop in mid and late life precisely because people become more keenly aware that life is short. Such people may find themselves becoming more adept in separating out the important from the trivial. Responsiveness to nature, human warmth, children, music, beauty in any form, may be heightened.'[1]

This elementality enhances the love life of many older people, who enjoy a heightening of the quality of their sex lives, which more than compensates for any decrease in its quality. Lovers gain in confidence and experience. They lose their inhibitions and impetuousness and frequently become more sensitive and caring. As a result sex assumes a far greater significance and depth. 'At seventeen it was an automatic reaction;' reported one man, 'at forty-three it is a joyous celebration of life.'

This sexual renaissance is more readily seen in women than in men. Maybe it takes longer for them to overcome their childhood inhibitions. Perhaps they have more vitality after the menopause, when their energy is no longer sapped by the drain of regular menstruation. Or it could be that their sexuality flourishes when they no longer have the responsibility of children, or the fear of an unwanted pregnancy. There is even a distinct possibility that there may be a hormonal explanation for the increase in libido which so many post-menopausal women enjoy. This was explained by Dr Helen Kaplan, who wrote: 'From a purely physiological standpoint, libido should theoretically *increase* at menopause, because the action of the woman's androgens, which is not materially affected by menopause, is unopposed by oestrogen.'[2]

Certainly, whatever the reason, most women find that age brings about an increase in their sexual enjoyment. Libido often blossoms, too. This was the majority verdict of the older women who replied to Shere Hite's survey. 'I didn't know getting older would make sex better! I'm fifty-one now and just getting started!' replied one. Another typical response was: 'I am sixty-six and sexual desire has not diminished. The enjoyment is as great as ever.'[3] Sometimes this sexual rejuvenation can cause problems, especially when women are widowed or married to men whose health is poor.

To Know You is to Love You

Time, as well as increasing sexual satisfaction, also improves the quality of long-term relationships. This is when the duity proves its worth.

Youngsters may have the freedom to establish temporary liaisons, but a one-night stand can never afford the cosiness and mutual understanding of a lifetime love affair. Casual sex is ephemeral and impersonal. It treats the other partner as a sex object rather than as an individual. When we enter a long-term relationship we are far more discriminating. We exercise our freedom of choice, to select one person and refuse all others. Providing we are reasonable judges of character, we select a person with whom we have a good chance of achieving happiness, emotional harmony, mental rapport and sexual fulfilment. The longer we live together, the closer our understanding should become, and the greater our ability to meet each other's sexual needs. As a result the leisurely sex life of a seventy-year-old can be infinitely richer than that of youngsters in their insecure and harried twenties.

He's Dead but He Won't Lie Down

Many famous men have maintained an active sex life well into their eighties, an age when it's often far easier to resist temptation than to find it. Some were still chasing girls at ninety, even though they couldn't remember why. When Victor Hugo was eighty his young grandson discovered him in bed with a youthful laundress. Not in the slightest embarrassed, Hugo looked up and said: 'Look, little Georges, that's what they call genius!' Three years later Hugo died, but his diary shows that even though his health was failing, he still found time and energy for sex on at least eight separate occasions in the last four months of his life.

Eminent musicians, such as Franz Liszt and Leopold Stokowski, have also found that neither their love of music nor their passion for sex diminished when they were past their allotted threescore and ten. And when conductor Pierre Monteux was interviewed on his ninetieth birthday and asked what he did when he wasn't conducting, he replied: 'I still have two abiding pleasures. One is my model railway, the other is women. But at ninety I find myself a little too old for model railways.'

It appears natural for men to maintain an interest in sex throughout their entire lives, providing they are physically fit and mentally active. This was one of Captain Cook's revelations when he visited the Polynesian Islands and found that King Lapetamaka II of Tonga, although in his ninth decade, was still faithfully carrying out his regal duties of deflowering all the island maidens, a ceremonial task which he sometimes performed eight times a day. Even more remarkable was the case of Thomas Parr, one of Britain's longest-living men, who at the age of 120 married a middle-aged widow. She claimed that she 'had never noticed her husband's great age, so well had he performed his conjugal duties'.

Surveys show that these are by no means exceptional cases. In my experience, the major deficiency in the sex lives of elderly men is not a shortage of libido but a lack of opportunity. They have the will but, being short of geriatric play-mates, often lack the way. One of my patients in his mid-nineties had this problem, and asked if he could have his girlie magazines sent to me rather than to his home address, so they wouldn't be intercepted by his family.

Children don't like to think of their parents having sex, especially when they are not in the first flush of youth. (Do they imagine that they themselves are immaculate conceptions?) This prejudice is maintained on radio phone-in programmes, where sex among the elderly is a taboo topic which causes just as much embarrassment as talk of love among the physically disabled or mentally handicapped. The male who enjoys a lusty sex life in his early twenties is admired as a dashing Lothario, but if it's discovered that he's still active in his seventies he's immediately condemned as a dirty old man. Why the change in outlook?

We like to pretend that sex is of no interest to the older generation, and yet at this very moment the world's geriatric homes are throbbing with carnal capers. At every hour, at some point on the globe, a nonogenarian will be adding an extra notch to his Zimmer frame. (A matron of one old folks' home told me that the tell-tale sign of these eventide romances was the appearance of two sets of false teeth on the bedside table.)

Most of these liaisons will be stable love affairs, but a number will be merely passing passions, and a few even commercial contracts. A short while ago detectives from the Hungarian vice squad arrested an eighty-seven-year-old woman and her ninety-three-year-old boyfriend for running a brothel in a state nursing home. 'Mrs Vlaczy was turning more than a dozen tricks a week,' said a police spokesman. 'Men were rolling up in wheelchairs outside a linen closet five at a time. Vlasjic Tzabo, her boyfriend, was standing at the door collecting money.' The woman believed that the service she offered was meeting a need as well as helping to supplement her old-age pension. Also, she told the vice squad officers, 'it was fun and kept me young.'[4]

There are no statistics for the number of elderly men using the services of prostitutes, but a Danish survey has revealed that 23 per cent of men over the age of ninety still masturbate.[5] In normal conditions the sex urge, like the urge to eat and drink, persists throughout life. This is one pleasure which lasts, while others fade. At ninety your failing eyesight may make reading difficult. Your joints may be too stiff for downhill skiing; your breath too short for underwater swimming. Too much alcohol upsets your liver; too much food gives you indigestion. But the joy of sex still remains. That's why it's so important to enhance your sexual vitality *now*, because in twenty or thirty years time it may be one of your few remaining sources of pleasure. You may even find that sexual conquests become easier as you grow older. Perhaps the grey hairs will inspire confidence and trust. This was the experience of Arthur Rubinstein, who told reporters: 'When I was young I used to have successes with women because I was young. Now I have successes with women because I am old. Middle age was the hardest part.'

Age may bring changes in our physiological performance, but the restrictions which nature imposes are nothing compared with the limitations we place on ourselves. Some older men are impotent because they are overweight; others because they are too tired or under excessive stress. (An American study of men over the age of sixty-five revealed that the professions with the highest rate of impotence were stressful occupations like those of doctors, and even more so journalists, publishers and editors.[6]) Others are impotent simply because they have lost confidence in their potency. They can be helped by reassurance, psychotherapy, placebo pills or faith healing.

One elderly couple were listening to a healing service on the radio conducted by a well-known revivalist preacher. After an impassioned sermon the preacher asked his sick listeners to join him in proving the healing power of faith. To transmit the restorative force they were instructed to place one hand on the radio and the other on the affected part of their bodies. She immediately followed his instructions and placed one hand on the radio and the other on her arthritic knee. Turning to her husband, she spotted him shyly placing one hand on the radio and the other on his crotch. 'It's no good doing that,' she said scornfully. 'He said he was going to heal the sick, not raise the dead.'

Sickness is the other major reason for waning sex drive. This was clearly shown when Swedish researchers selected a group of sexually active seventy-year-old married men and followed them up five years later. By the time of the second interview all were still married, but one in five had ceased to lead a normal sex life. The major reasons were stress and illnesses such as high blood pressure, diabetes and heart disease.[7] In these cases the flame of love is quenched long before the lamp is drained of oil.

Even where serious illness intervenes, it may not be an inevitable cause of impotence. Many men believe that, because of their failing health, they are totally incapable of getting an erection. In some cases this may be true; but in many others it is not. The acid test is the presence or absence of erections during sleep, known medically as nocturnal penile tumescence (NPT), which occur approximately every ninety minutes during the night. If NPT occurs, the impotence is purely relative. But if dream sleep occurs, with the tell-tale movements of the eyeballs, *without* the accompanying NPT, it is likely that the impotence is absolute, with a pathological cause.

Nowadays it is possible to measure NPT in sleep laboratories with an instrument known as a plethysmograph. A simpler measure, used by doctors before the development of the plethysmograph, is the postage stamp test. This is a suitable test for home use by men with erection problems. The instructions are simple: before you fall asleep, paste a ring of postage stamps around your flaccid penis and don a pair of briefs to hold the loop in place. The next morning you should wake to find the ring broken (unless you've been delivered to a distant postal address). This proves that you are still capable of achieving an erection, even if you find it difficult to do so at the appropriate time. If the ring remains intact, it is advisable to consult your doctor to see if there are organic reasons behind the lack of NPT.

We've Only Just Begun

If the young find it difficult to imagine grandpa watching blue movies, they find it even more difficult to visualise grandma having an exciting sex life. But many women find their interest in sex increases as they grow older, and a number become orgasmic for the first time in their sixties and seventies. Where sex is concerned, many women are late developers. In practice, this gives rise to problems, since many women are widowed at the very time when they are reaching their erotic peak. This often brings their love life to an abrupt halt, since they were brought up in age when 'nice' girls didn't shop around for male partners – a licence which was even more unthinkable for respectable elderly ladies. According to a long-term study of geriatric sexual behaviour carried out at Duke University, North Carolina, 90 per cent of women stop having intercourse when their husbands die, fall ill or become impotent. 'By contrast,' the researchers noted, 'marital status had little or no effect on reported incidence of sexual activity among elderly men.'[8] It seems that a double standard exists in adulthood as well as in youth, with women being far more faithful to their long-term partners.

To compensate for this some elderly women develop an active fantasy life. Others shower their love on pets. One little old lady was sitting in front of an open fire nursing her tom cat on her lap when a fairy appeared and offered her a solitary wish, which could be anything her heart desired – youth, beauty or wealth. The lady had lost her husband long ago and had no doubt what she wanted: 'I'd like my tom cat to be turned into a beautiful young man.' The fairy waved her wand and immediately the cat became transformed into a glorious specimen of manhood, who walked towards her, gently kissed her cheek and then whispered in her ear: 'Now aren't you sorry that you took me to the vet?'

Others, who are not satisfied by a world of fantasy, masturbate. This practice is far more common among older women than is generally imagined, according to a survey carried out by the Consumer Union, which revealed that fully a third of American women over the age of seventy masturbate.[9] What would the neighbours think if they knew such things were going on next door? And what an appalling waste of affection and love this isolation brings. The 'divine' Sarah Bernhardt was reputed to have had thousands of love affairs and at one time was said to have seduced all the current European heads of state. Most of her leading men fell in love with her and continued to do so when she was no longer young enough to play the ingenue roles. When she was sixty-six, she toured America with a Dutch-born actor who was thirty-five years her junior. This was the start of a passionate four-year romance, which many years later the young actor referred to in his autobiography as 'the most glorious four years of my life'. Such is the love that the older woman can give. At this age she is often particularly attractive to younger men, because she is confident, considerate, experienced – and grateful.

Young at Heart

Sex among elderly couples often falters because it loses its zest. This is sometimes caused by boredom, a subject treated at length earlier in this book. This can be overcome by introducing the aphrodisiac of change, without looking for the novelty and stimulus of outside relationships for, as Balzac observed: 'It is as absurd to say that a man can't love one woman all the time as it is to say that a violinist needs several violins to play the same piece of music.'

191

Sexercise 22
The Play Pen

Relationships suffer when they become too sober and staid. To be serious about sex at twenty is unfortunate; to be equally serious about it at seventy can be calamitous. Sex is fun. It is not just a mechanical coupling, it is also a time for lighthearted fore*play*, tickling, teasing and ribald banter. Horseplay is a regular part of teenage courtship, and merits an equally prominent place in the wooing of older couples. Elderly lovers need their fun and games, even if their romps are under the blankets rather than in the hay. At seventy, Jack should still be chasing the girls, even if he only does so when it's downhill.

When psychiatrist Erik Erikson carried out a thirty-year study of a sample group of Americans he found that the adults leading the most interesting, fulfilling lives were the ones who managed to keep a sense of playfulness at the centre of their lives.[10] The need to maintain this jocose attitude to life was recognised by the Greek philosophers. When Plato asked himself the rhetorical question 'How should life be lived?' he gave the immediate and unequivocal answer 'Life should be lived as play.'

This lighthearted approach needs to pervade our entire lives. Abraham Maslow, one of the founding fathers of humanistic psychology, noted that emotionally mature people are characterised by their merriment and gaiety. It is typical of them, he said, 'that they can enjoy themselves in love and in sex. Sex very frequently becomes a game in which laughter is quite as common as panting.'[11]

Find time for spontaneous play and your sex life will become an exciting feast rather than basic bed and bored. Recapture the fun and games, the frivolity and teasing, and you'll find that the more happily you play together, the more contentedly you'll lay together.

Many of the deprivations of age – the shortage of breath, the muscular weakness, the weakening bone texture, the failing memory – are the results of disuse atrophy. Our functions decline, not in accordance with some preordained divine plan, but because we fail to sustain them. This is particularly true of our sex drive, which is best preserved by regular use. Disused organs waste, and this applies to testicles, ovaries and vaginas as well as brain cells and muscle fibres. At the age of seventy-one publisher Helen Gurney Brown wrote a book, *The Late Show*, in which she offered women over fifty a variety of practical survival tips, such as stretching an ageing and under-used vagina with a lubricated banana. She recognised that the vaginal muscles shorten if they are not subjected to regular stretching.

Masters and Johnson were equally insistent that sex was the finest prophylactic for ageing males who wanted to preserve their libido. 'Use it, or lose it', was their chief recommendation, and they were encouraged to find that when sexual dysfunction is caused by disuse atrophy it can normally be reversed. 'The male over fifty years old can be trained out of his secondarily acquired impotence in a high percentage of cases,' they report.[12]

At Twilight Time

One method of sexual rejuvenation for men, enshrined in ancient folklore, is shunamitism. This is the practice of sleeping with young girls. King David tried the remedy on his deathbed, but he was too debilitated to respond to the stimulus of being placed side by side in bed with the young Shunamite virgin Abishag. He inhaled her breath as instructed, but because of his enfeebled condition he 'knew her not'. The cure was of greater benefit to L. Claudius Hernip, a virile elderly gentleman who, according to the inscription on his tombstone, 'lived one hundred and fifteen years with the aid of the breath of young women, to the surprise of physicians'. The engraver was so impressed by Hernip's record that he carved a postscript to the epitaph: 'Lead your life accordingly'.

One eighty-eight-year-old man decided to follow this advice and went to his doctor for a check-up before marrying a girl more than forty years his junior. The doctor found him to be in good health, but nevertheless did his very best to dissuade him from the marriage. When this proved of no avail he gave the old man some advice. 'If you want to keep your marriage intact and your wife happy I suggest you take a young lodger.' Some months later they met at a cocktail party and the patient, now nearing his ninetieth birthday, proudly told his doctor that his wife was expecting a baby. 'So at least you followed my advice and took a young lodger,' the doctor responded.

'Oh, sure,' the old man replied with a mischievous grin, 'and she's pregnant too!'

Shunamitism is sometimes regarded as idle superstition, or a subject fit only for bar-room jokes, but there is evidence that it works for laboratory animals. Tests show that male rats live longer if they are given the company of young females, even if they don't copulate with them. The same may apply to humans, according to a study into the 'life-enhancing qualities of the younger wife' carried out by researchers from the University of Oklahoma. They analysed the national mortality figures and discovered that the death rate for men with younger wives was 13 per cent lower than the national average, compared with the death rate of men with older wives, which was 20 per cent above the norm. This seems to confirm the popular notion that men like Fred Astaire or Cary Grant look so good and live so long because they are living with younger women. (Both men are now dead, but at the time of the study Fred Astaire was living with a wife forty-five years his junior, while Barbara Grant was forty-eight years younger than husband Cary.)[13] The researchers suggested that there might be a 'pre-marital factor' at work whereby healthy men select, or are selected by, younger women. But they also believe that a 'post-marital factor' operates whereby the stimulus of living with a young mate proves 'psychologically, physiologically or socially beneficial'.

The study was limited to the longevity of men, a bias which is symptomatic of our different attitude towards male and female sexuality. With the double standards which exist, we still find it easier to accept the marriage of an older man and young woman than the liaison of an older woman and a young man, whom we automatically dismiss as a 'toyboy'. Yet the latter is physiologically more easily justified, for age does more to lessen the libido of men than to diminish the sex drive of women. This was confirmed by Masters and Johnson who wrote: 'There is no time limit drawn by the advancing years for female sexuality.'

The Times They Are A-changing

At seventy women are expected to settle down to a life of sexless domesticity, but at this age most of my lady patients tell me that they still find sex far more exciting than flower-arranging and crochet.

Unfortunately, however desperate their loneliness and however great their sexual longing, most would not contemplate having an affair with a man thirty years their junior. They would be concerned at the reaction of their family and friends, and worried that their bodies would not stand up to the close inspection of their young lovers. (Helen Gurney Brown recommends removing his glasses long before you retire to the

194

bedroom and expose your cellulite.)

Many young men have had reason to praise the expertise and zest of their more mature lovers. According to Ian Fleming: 'Older women are best because they always think they are doing it for the last time.' At their age they are enthusiastic because they know they run the dreadful risk that if they resist temptation now it may never come again.

Sex at seventy is not 'abnormal' or 'undignified' as some people suggest – it is a vital ingredient of a hale, whole and healthy life. Numerous geriatric surveys have been carried out which agree on two essential points. The first is that sexual activity can persist throughout life. And the second is that often it doesn't. All too frequently it disappears because we are conditioned by our culture to anticipate and accept its disappearance. This belief is not found in other social settings, such as among the centenarians living in the Caucasian mountains of Georgia, the Andean villages of Ecuador or the Hunza valley in Kashmir. The American gerontologist Dr Alexander Leaf, of Harvard University Medical School, has visited each of these centres of extreme longevity and has returned convinced that 'a vigorous life – sexual activity included – was possible for up to a hundred years.'

Till the End of Time

Sexual vitality is not an isolated attribute, it is an integral part of our personality. People are consistent in their lifestyles and energy output. If they are lethargic in the office and indolent in their off-duty hours, they are likely to be every bit as sluggish in the bedroom. Conversely, if they are dynamic at work and zestful at play they are likely to be equally lively lovers.

Mankind has evolved over several millennia as a high-activity species. The forces which shaped our destiny prepared us for an existence in the primeval forests – a life of challenge, excitement and ceaseless movement. We are ill equipped to withstand the passivity of our modern civilisation, with its routine chores and sedentary lifestyle. Urban life provides too little stimulus, too little physical activity.

The epidemic diseases we suffer today – chronic fatigue, depression, back pain, heart disease, obesity, premature ageing – are all related to our sedentary way of life. They have been called the hypokinetic diseases, because they are the result of under-activity. Loss of libido is one of these diseases, as I argued in an earlier book called *Fit For Life* (see page 211).

'All desirable traits in a human being correlate positively,' wrote psychologist Abraham Maslow. Cultivate a love of life and you'll reap a life of love. When Sarah Bernhardt was in her seventies she was asked when she intended to quit her sexual activities. 'When I draw my last breath,' she replied. 'I hope to live as I have always lived. The strength of my energy and vitality lies entirely in their subservience to my destiny as a woman.'

Sexercise 23
The Zest Fest

If you want to recapture your *joie de vivre* step up your general activity level. This will enable you to lose weight, make you less prone to heart disease and help you to enjoy a more vigorous sex life. Why be fat when it's just as easy to be slim? Why be tired when you could be brimming over with vitality? Why resign yourself to being an octogenarian has-been, when many of your contemporaries are skiing and climbing mountains? Why suffer a loss of libido when you could be enjoying a sex life full of vigour, fun and youthful exuberance?

Cultivate a zest for life and you will discover the secret of well-being, success and happiness, for as Montaigne said: '*La seule morale est de vivre avec ferveur.*' (The sole principle is to live with passion.)

And so, as I come to the end of this book, I return to its beginning. Sex is the well-spring of life. Sex is energy. Sex is fun. Sex is rejuvenating. Sex is forever. Long live love!

SUMMARY
- If you're past middle age you'll find you'll get more enjoyment out of life in general, and sex in particular, if you take time to savour its pleasures.
- The decline in sexual function which some elderly people suffer is sometimes no more than a self-fulfilling prophecy. They lose libido because they *expect* their amorous powers to wane. Don't allow yourself to be short-changed. Surveys show that the sex urge can persist throughout life, just like the urge to eat and drink.
- Illness is one of the commonest causes of loss of sex drive among the elderly. If you've lost your get-up-and-go, get your doctor to give

you a general check-up to make sure you're not suffering from some hidden ailment, like diabetes.

- If your relationship is growing stale, bring back the sparkle by introducing a little fun and games, slap-and-tickle, horseplay and banter.
- Many of the infirmities of old age – muscle weakness, shortage of breath, lack of libido – are the result of disuse atrophy. Whatever your age, whether seventeen or seventy, there is only one way to maintain peak sexual function, and that is to submit it to regular use.
- Life must be lived with passion. If you're vigorous in your everyday activities, you'll be equally vigorous in your loving. Follow the programme in this book and you can expect to maintain this vitality and drive throughout your entire life, for as gerontologist Dr Alexander Leaf affirmed a vigorous life – sexual activity included – is possible for up to a hundred years.

Notes

One   Begin the Beguine

1. *Chief Executive*, September 1986.
2. Schiavi, R.C. et al, *Hormones and Behaviour* 1989, 23, p. 221.
3. Pearson, P., *Super Marital Sex* 1987, London: Futura, p. 272.
4. Lief, H.I., in *Contemporary Sexual Behaviour: Critical Issues in the 1970s* 1973, Baltimore: John Hopkins University Press, pp. 441–53.
5. Baudouin, C., *Suggestion and Autosuggestion* 1920, London: George Allen & Unwin, p. 116.
6. Coué, E., *Self Mastery Through Conscious Autosuggestion* 1922, London: Allen and Unwin Ltd.
7. Stopes, M.C., *Enduring Passion* 1936, London: Putnam & Co.
8. De Ropp, R.S., *Sex Energy* 1970 London: Jonathan Cape, p. 103.
9. Sacks, O., *Awakenings* 1973, London: Duckworth.

Two   The Power of Love

1. Quoted by H. Greenwald and I. Greenwald in *The Sex Life Letters* 1986, London: Grafton Books, p. 105.
2. Fromm, E., quoted in *The Journal of Personality and Social Psychology* 1991, vol. 60, 3, pp. 435–38.
3. Quoted in *The Sex Life Letters*, by H. Greenwald and I. Greenwald 1986, London: Grafton Books, p. 134.
4. Reich, W., *The Function of the Orgasm* 1968, London: Panther Books, p. 128.
5. Huxley, T.H., quoted Castle, E.B. *Ancient Education and Today* 1961, London: Penguin Books, p. 196.
6. Kaplan, H., *Disorders of Sexual Desire* 1979, London: Baillière Tindall, p. 79.

Three Two Sleepy People

1. Hilliard, M., *A Woman Doctor Looks at Life and Love*.
2. *Health Education* 1956, London: HMSO.
3. Pearson, P., *Super Marital Sex* 1988, London: Futura, p. vii.
4. Ginsberg, S.W., in *An Analysis of the Kinsey Reports* 1954, New York: Mentor Books, p. 38.
5. *The Kama Sutra* 1963 ed., London: Panther Books, p. 38.
6. Walker, W., *Body Magic* 1979, London: Granada Publishing, p. 184.
7. Sheldon, W.H., *The Varieties of Human Physique* 1940, New York: Harper.
8. Beller, A.S., *Fat and Thin* 1977, New York: Farrar, Straus and Giroux, pp. 74.
9. Beller, A.S., ibid. p. 63.
10. Giese, H. and Schmidt, A., *Studenten Sexualtat* 1968, Hamburg: Rowohlt.
11. Steinbech, M., quoted in *London Evening Standard*, 16 August 1973.
12. *Sunday Telegraph*, 9 February 1992.
13. Desmond, A. and Moore, J., *Darwin* 1992, London: Penguin Books.
14. Cattier, M., *The Life and Work of Wilhelm Reich* 1971, New York: Horizon Press, p. 158.
15. Goldberg, B.Z., *The Sacred Fire* 1974, Secaucus, New Jersey: The Citadel Press, p. 270.

Four Let Yourself Go

1. *The Sunday Times*, 10 January 1993.
2. Gifford, E.S., *The Charms of Love* 1962, New York: Doubleday, p. 35.
3. Cauthery, P. and Cole, M., *The Fundamentals of Sex* 1971, London: W. H. Allen, p. 90.
4. *Psychology Today*, October 1978.
5. Kaplan, H.S., *Disorders of Sexual Desire* 1979, London: Ballière Tindall, p. 10.
6. Kliver, H. and Bucy, P.C., *Archives of Neurology and Psychiatry* 42, pp. 979–1000.
7. Schriener, L. and Kling, A., *Journal of Neurophysiology* 16, pp. 643–59.

8. Eysenck, H.J., *Sex and Personality* 1978, London: Abacus, p. 148.
9. Olsen, E., in *Child Abuse and Neglect: Cross Cultural Perspectives* 1991, Berkeley Ca.: University of California Press.
10. *New Scientist*, 8 March 1973.
11. Kaplan, H.S., ibid. p. 83.
12. Kaplan, H.S., ibid. p. 83.
13. Friday, N., *My Secret Garden* 1974, New York: Pocket Books and *Men in Love* 1980, London: Arrow Books.

Five   Give Me Five Minutes More

1. Willy, A. et al, *The Practice of Sex* 1939, London: Francis Aldor, p. 76.
2. Bettelheim, B., *Symbolic Wounds* 1962, New York: Collier Books.
3. Harlow, H.F., *American Psychologist* 1958, 13, p. 637–85.
4. O'Connor, D., *How to Put the Love Back into Making Love* 1989, London: Columbus Books, p. 34.
5. Gillies, J., *Transcendental Sex* 1978, New York: Holt, Rinehart & Winston, p. 120.
6. Reeves, D., *For God's Sake* 1988, London: Font Paperbacks, p. 79.
7. Hutin, S., *Casting Spells* 1973, London: Barrie & Jenkins Ltd, p. 81.
8. Sabazius, Father, *Envoutement et Contre-evolutement* 1937.

Six   Enjoy Yourself, It's Later Than You Think

1. Olds, J., quoted in *The Pleasure Areas* by H.J. Campbell 1973, London: Eyre Methuen, p. 26.
2. Beebe-Center, J.G., *The Psychology of Pleasantness and Unpleasantness* 1932, New York: Van Nostrand.
3. Lynch, J.F., and McCarthy, J.P., *Psychophysiology* 1969, pp. 389–93.
4. Thayer, R.E., *Psychology Reports* 1978, 42, pp. 747–56.
5. *Journal of Neurology, Neurosurgery and Psychiatry* 1992, 55, pp. 247–50.
6. Hutton, B., *Psychology Today*, November 1976.
7. Hall, R., *Marie Stopes: A Biography* 1977, London: Virago, p. 288.
8. Hite, S., *The Hite Report* 1977, New York: Summit Books.
9. Van de Velde, T.H., *Ideal Marriage* 1955, London: Heinemann, p. 249.

10. Turner, E.S., *Taking the Cure* 1967, London: Michael Joseph, p. 57.
11. Tisserand, R., *The Art of Aromatherapy* 1985, Essex: C.W. Daniel Company Ltd, p. 238.
12. Maury, M., *The Secret of Life and Youth* 1964, London: C.W. Daniel.

Seven Soft Lights and Sweet Music

1. *Independent*, 5 March 1987.
2. Mutwa, C., *Writings of a Zulu Witch-Doctor* 1971, London: Penguin Books, p. 206.
3. *The Sunday Times*, 15 February 1981.
4. Gifford, E.S., *The Charms of Love* 1962, New York: Doubleday & Co. Inc., p. 49.

Eight Sometimes When We Touch

1. Hite, S., *The Hite Report* 1977, New York: Summit Books, p. 556.
2. Hite, S., *The Hite Report on Male Sexuality* 1981, London: Macdonald Futura, p. 324.
3. Lynch, J.J., *The Broken Heart* 1977, New York: Basic Books Inc.
4. Morris, D., *Intimate Behaviour* 1971, London: Corgi, p. 243.
5. O'Connor, D., *How to Put the Love Back into Making Love* 1989, London: Columbus Books Ltd, p. xiii.
6. Jourard, S.M., *British Journal of Social and Clinical Psychology* 1966, 5, p. 221.
7. Edwards, A. and Husted, E.J., *Journal of Clinical Psychology* 1977, 32, 3, p. 697.
8. *Sun*, 21 November 1974.
9. Morris, H., *The Art of Kissing* 1977, London: Pan Books.
10. *Time*, 28 January 1985.
11. Montagu, A., *Touching* 1977, New York: Harper & Row, p. 36.
12. Roth, L.L. and Rosenblatt, J.S., *Science* 1965, 151, p. 1403.
13. Konner, M.J., *Ethological Studies of Child Behaviour* 1972, Cambridge: The University Press, p. 285.
14. Hite, S., *The Hite Report on Male Sexuality* 1978, London: Macdonald Futura, p. 551.
15. O'Connor, D., ibid. p. 129.

Nine Sweet and Lovely

1. *Time*, 23 May 1978.
2. *Daily Telegraph*, 15 February 1993.
3. *Nature* 1976, 260, p. 5551.
4. Schiffman, S.S., *New England Journal of Medicine* 308, 22, pp. 1337–43.
5. *Daily Telegraph*, 21 December 1979.
6. Gonzales-Crussi, F., *The Five Senses* 1990, London: Pan Books, p. 72.
7. *Time*, 16 July 1979.
8. *The Sunday Times*, 21 January 1990.
9. Kuno, Y., *Physiology of Human Perspiration* 1935, London.
10. Malinowski, B., *The Sexual Life of Savages* 1929, London: Routledge, p. 378.
11. Lake, M., *Scents and Sensuality* 1989, London: Futura, p. 12.
12. *Daily Telegraph*, 26 November 1992.
13. Williams, L., *Man and Monkey* 1967, London: André Deutsch Ltd, p. 50.
14. Jacobs, E., *British Journal of Sexual Medicine* quoted in *Medical Observer*, Sydney, 31 July 1987, p. 35.

Ten I Only Have Eyes for You

1. Hite, S., *The Hite Report on Male Sexuality* 1978, London: Macdonald, p. 104.
2. Malinowski, B., *The Sexual Life of Savages* 1929, London: Routledge, p. 141.
3. Fast, J., *Body Language* 1970, London: Pan Books, p. 142.
4. Rubin, Z., *Liking and Loving: An Introduction to Social Psychology* 1973, New York: Holt, Rinehart & Winston.
5. Centers, R., *Journal of Psychology* 1972, 82, p. 111.
6. *Village Voice* quoted in *Love's Mysteries* 1976, London: Open Books, p. 24.
7. Zunin, L. and Zunin, N., *Contact: The First Four Minutes* 1972, Los Angeles: Nash Publishing, p. 117.
8. Clore, G. et al, *Journal of Consulting and Clinical Psychology* 1975, 43, p. 491.
9. Douglas, J., *The Nude Beach* 1977, New York: Sage.
10. Greenwald, H. and Greenwald, R., *The Sex Life Letters* 1986, London: Grafton Books, p. 220.

11. Friday, N., *My Secret Garden* 1976, New York: Pocket Books, p. 106.
12. Fisher, W. and Byrne, D., *Psychology Today*, December 1977.
13. Weidner, G. et al, *Psychology Today*, September 1979.

Eleven They're Playing Our Song

1. Campbell, H.J., *The Pleasure Areas* 1973, London: Eyre Methuen, p. 46.
2. *National Geographical Magazine*, December 1988, p. 903.
3. Sparks, J., *The Sexual Connection* 1977, London: Sphere Books, p. 82.
4. Van de Velde, T.H., *Ideal Marriage* 1943, London: Heinemann, p. 250.
5. Greenwald, H. and Greenwald, R., *The Sex Life Letters* 1986, London: Grafton Books p. 150.
6. Hite, S., *The Hite Report* 1977, New York: Summit Books, p. 598.
7. *The Encyclopedia of Sexual Behaviour* 1961, London: The Corsano Co. Ltd, p. 747.
8. ibid. p. 752.
9. Hartogs, R., *Four-Letter Word Games* 1967, New York: M. Evans, p. 72.
10. Goldberg, B.Z., *The Sacred Fire* 1974, Secaucus, New Jersey: The Citadel Press, p. 77.
11. Willy, A. et al, *The Practice of Sex* 1939, London: Francis Aldor, p. 69 and p. 83.
12. *Mail on Sunday*, 8 April 1990.

Twelve Blaze Away

1. Bokun, B., *Humour Therapy* 1986, Vita Books.
2. Sargent, W., *The Unquiet Mind* 1967, London: Pan Books, p. 167.
3. Dutton, D.G. and Aron, A.P., *Journal of Personality and Social Psychology* 1975, 30, 4, p. 510.
4. Wincze, J.P. et al, *Journal of Abnormal Psychology* 1979, 86, 1.

Thirteen Ready, Willing and Able

1. Friedman, M., *Buried Alive: The Biography of Janis Joplin* 1973,

New York: William Morrow & Co., p. 70.
2. Walker, B., *Sex and the Supernatural* 1970, New York: Ottenheimer Publishers Inc., p. 18.
3. Chesser, E., *Love without Fear* 1941, London: Rich and Cowan Medical Publications, p. 11.
4. Kaplan, H.S., *Disorders of Sexual Desire* 1979, London: Ballière Tindall, p. 4.
5. Quoted in *Emotions: Their Parameters and Measurements* 1975, New York: Raven Press, p. 165.
6. Arguelles, A.E. et al, *Proceedings of the 16th International Congress of Aerospace Medicine* 1978, London.
7. Hilliard, M., *Woman and Fatigue: A Woman Doctor's Answer* 1960, London: Macmillan.
8. *The Sunday Times*, 7 May 1978.
9. Eysenck, H.J., *Sex and Personality* 1978, London: Sphere Books Ltd, p. 92.
10. Pearce, P.L., *The Social Psychology of Tourist Behaviour* 1982, Oxford: Pergamon Press.
11. *The Sunday Times*, 21 December 1986.
12. Butler, R.N. and Lewis, M.I., *Love and Sex After 40* 1986, New York: Harper and Row.

Fourteen   Fit as a Fiddle and Ready for Love

1. Rowse, A.C., *Simon Forman* 1974, London: Weidenfeld & Nicolson.
2. Stopes, M.C., *Enduring Passion* 2nd ed. 1929, London: Putnam & Co. Ltd, p. 108.
3. Hite, S., *The Hite Report on Male Sexuality* 1978, London: Macdonald Futura, p. 867.
4. Wilson, G. and Nias, D., *Love's Mysteries* 1976, London: Open Books, p. 76.
5. Quoted in *Reader's Digest*, July 1992 p. 61.
6. Quoted in *Jogging* magazine, April 1979 p. 27.
7. *The Runner's Handbook* 1978, London: Penguin Books.
8. Berscheid, E. et al, *Journal of Experimental Social Psychology* 1971, 7, p. 173.
9. Soyka, F., *The Ion Effect* 1977, London: Bantam Books.
10. Pearson, P., *Super Marital Sex* 1988, London: Ebury Press, p. 194.
11. D'Angerville, M., *The Private Life of Louis XV* 1924, London: John Lane.

Fifteen Doing What Comes Naturally

1. Schiavi, R.C. et al, *Psychosomatic Medicine* 1988, 50, pp. 304–18.
2. Campbell, H.J., *The Pleasure Areas* 1973, London: Eyre Methuen, p. 37.
3. *MD* magazine, vol. 5, September 1961.
4. De Kruif, P., *The Male Hormone* 1945, New York: Harcourt Brace & Co.
5. Wilson, G. and Nias, D., *Love's Mysteries: The Psychology of Sexual Attraction* 1976, London: Open Books.
6. Loraine, J.A., *Sex and the Population Crisis* 1970, London: Heinemann Medical Books Ltd.
7. Quoted in *The Sunday Times*, 11 March 1972.
8. *GP* magazine, 1 April 1983, p. 26.
9. *Daily Telegraph*, 30 March 1993.
10. Belham, G., *The Virility Diet* 1965, London: Wolfe Publishing.
11. Turner, E.S., *Taking the Cure* 1967, London: Michael Joseph, p. 93.
12. *European*, 22 March 1993.
13. Myserson, A. and Neustadt, R., *Endocrinology* 1939, 25, 7.

Sixteen Love Potion Number Nine

1. Van Thiel et al., *Science* 1974, vol. 186, p. 941.
2. Gordon, G.G. et al, *New England Journal of Medicine* 1976, 295, pp. 793–7.
3. Wilson, G. and Nias, D., *Love's Mysteries: The Science of Sexual Attraction* 1976, London: Open Books.
4. Ellis, A. and Abarbanel, A. (eds), *The Encyclopedia of Sexual Behaviour* 1961, London: The Corsano Co., p. 78.
5. Atkins, R.A., *Super-Energy Diet* 1978, London: Bantam Books, p. 188.
6. Quoted in the *Daily Telegraph*, 14 August 1989.
7. Bryce-Smith, D. and Hodgkinson, L., *The Zinc Solution* 1986, London: Arrow p. 184.
8. *Harvard Letter* quoted in the *International Journal of Alternative and Complementary Medicine*, October 1992.
9. Popov, I., *Stay Young* 1975, New York: Grosset & Dunlap, p. 165.
10. Reported in *The Sunday Times*, 5 April 1981, p. 84.
11. Grieve, M., *A Modern Herbal* 1976, London: Penguin Books, p. 249.

12. Lake, M., *Scents and Sensuality* 1989, London: Futura, p. 26.

Seventeen Tea for Two

1. Lillar, S., *Aspects of Love* 1965, London: Thames & Hudson, p. 107.
2. May, R., *Love and Will* 1972, London: Fontana Library, p. 75.
3. Hite, S., *The Hite Report on Male Sexuality* 1978, London: Macdonald, p. 322.
4. Stopes, M., *Enduring Passion* 2nd ed. 1936, London: Putnam & Co.
5. Kaplan, H. *Disorders of Sexual Desire* 1979, London: Ballière Tindall, p. 90.
6. *Family Circle*, 13 March 1979.
7. Kaplan, H., ibid. p. 17.
8. Howard, W. and Dawes, R.M., *Personality and Social Psychology Bulletin* 1976, pp. 478–80.
9. Keidman, E., *Light His Fire* 1990, London: Piatkus, p. 196.
10. Greenwald, H. and Greenwald, R., *The Sex Life Letters* 1974, London: Grafton Books, p. 278.
11. Williams, L., *Man and Monkeys* 1967, New York: Lippincott, p. 42.
12. *The Sunday Times*, 30 June 1974.
13. Masters, W.H. and Johnson, V.E., *Human Sexual Response* 1966, London: Churchill.
14. Wilson, G. and Nias, D., *Love's Mysteries* 1976, London: Open Books, p. 105.
15. De Ropp, R.S., *Sex Energy* 1970, London: Jonathan Cape, p. 230.
16. Kreidman, E., ibid p. 107.

Eighteen For Every Man There's a Woman

1. Dartington, C.D., quoted in *The Sunday Times*, 27 August 1978.
2. Quoted in *Reader's Digest*, July 1984.
3. Willy, A. et al, *The Practice of Sex* 1939, London: Francis Aldor, p. 121.
4. Quoted in *The Sunday Times*, 18 April 1976.
5. *Journal of Social Psychology* 1976, vol. 99:1, p. 115.
6. Levi, L., *Stress and Distress* 1971, London: Oxford University Press.

7. Hite, S., *The Hite Report* 1977, London: Paul Hamlyn, p. 633.
8. Greenwald, H. and Greenwald, R., *The Sex Life Letters* 1986, London: Grafton Books, p. 445.
9. Naute, C. and Naute, D., *Wake up in Bed Together* 1973, New York: Stein and Day, pp. 34–46.
10. Quoted in *Sex Energy* 1970, London: Jonathan Cape, p. 83.
11. Masters, W.H. and Johnson, V.E., *Human Sexual Inadequacy* 1970, Boston: Little, Brown.
12. Morris, D., *Intimate Behaviour* 1972, London: Corgi, p. 36.
13. Penny, A. and Stephens, N.F., *How to Make Love to a Man*.
14. Eysenck, H.J., *Sex and Personality* 1978, London: Sphere Books, p. 40.
15. Ford, C.S. and Beach, F.A., *Patterns of Sexual Behaviour* 1951, New York: Harper Bros. & Paul Hoeber.
16. Albert, E., in *Man and Civilization Symposium* 1963, New York: McGraw Hill.

Nineteen   Our Love is Here to Stay

1. Butler, R.N., *Love and Sex after 40* 1986, Santa Barbara, California: Landmark Books.
2. Kaplan, H.S., *The New Sex Therapy* 1974, New York: Brunner, Mazel, p. 111.
3. Hite, S., *The Hite Report* 1977, New York: Summit Books, pp. 508–10.
4. *Daily Telegraph*, 9 May 1992.
5. *British Journal of Sexual Medicine* 1978, vol. 5, 32.
6. *The Sunday Times*, 1 February 1970.
7. Persson, G. and Svanborg, A., *Journal of the American Geriatric Society* 1992, 40, pp. 439–44.
8. *Reader's Digest*, May 1974, p. 176.
9. Butler, R., ibid. p. 209.
10. Erikson, E.H., *Childhood and Society* 1955, New York: Norton.
11. Maslow, A.H. in *The Meaning of Love* 1953, New York: The Julian Press Inc., pp. 57–93.
12. Masters, W.H. and Johnson, V.E., *Human Sexual Response* 1966 London: Churchill.
13. *Daily Mail*, 24 January 1985.

Libido Quotient
Questionnaire

This questionnaire is designed to help you estimate your Libido Quotient (LQ), which is a measure of the strength of your current sex drive. Scores vary considerably from person to person and there are therefore no 'ideal' or 'above average' scores. An LQ of 60 may be normal for you, but unusually low for your partner. If from time to time you and your partner measure your LQs you will be able to determine:

- Whether there is a marked difference in your sex drive – 'desire incongruity' – which can give rise to relationship problems if it is not recognised and handled sympathetically (see page 155).
- Whether your sex drive is dwindling. This is often an indication of lowered general health and can result from tiredness, stress or lack of physical fitness (see chapter fourteen).
- Whether you have taken full advantage of the sexercises in this book, which should result in an increase in your LQ score. (A fall in the scores at a later stage should act as a reminder to resume the sexercises.)

Answer all questions as honestly as you can, remembering that there are no *right* or *wrong* answers. In each case circle the letter on the right which most closely matches your true response:

A – Definitely true
B – True
C – Probably true
D – Not true
E – Definitely not true

1. It doesn't take much to get me
   sexually excited.   A   B   C   D   E

2. I sometimes find it hard to control
   my sexual feelings. A   B   C   D   E

3. Seeing a person in the nude
   doesn't interest me at all. A   B   C   D   E

4. When I stimulate my partner
   I get aroused very quickly. A   B   C   D   E

5. I sometimes go for weeks without
   experiencing sexual desire. A   B   C   D   E

6. I rarely think about sex during
   the working day. A   B   C   D   E

7. I find it embarrassing to talk about
   sex even with my partner. A   B   C   D   E

8. Sex is an important part
   of my life. A   B   C   D   E

9. I often find myself dwelling
   on sexual fantasies. A   B   C   D   E

10. I feel there is something lacking
    in my present sex life. A   B   C   D   E

Scoring
For questions 1, 2, 4, 8 and 9 score:
5 for every A
4 for every B
3 for every C
2 for every D
1 for every E
For questions 3, 5, 6, 7 and 10 score:
1 for every A
2 for every B
3 for every C
4 for every D
5 for every E

Useful Addresses

Counselling

RELATE provides a nationwide counselling service for people who are experiencing relationship difficulties. All of their counsellors are trained to help people with sexual problems, and 250 have been specially trained in psychosexual therapy. They can be contacted by telephoning a local RELATE office, or by writing or telephoning the RELATE head office:

RELATE,
Herbert Gray College,
Little Church Street,
Rugby CV21 3AP
(Tel: 0788 573241)

Food Supplement

Aphrogen, the food supplement mentioned in chapter sixteen, is available from selected chemists and health food stores, price £18.50 for a month's supply, or direct from:

Hi-Care Products Ltd,
30 Sycamore Road,
Amersham,
Bucks HP6 5DR
(Post and package free for deliveries in the UK.)

Air Ionisers

The Mountain Breeze range of air ionisers is Britain's bestselling negative ion generator. It is approved for electrical safety by the Electricity Council and carries a five-year guarantee. Free literature and details of local stockists can be obtained from:

Mountain Breeze Ionisers,
6 Priorswood Place,
Skelmersdale,
Lancs WN8 9QB
(Tel: 0695 21155)

Fit For Life

This lively book provides a blueprint for healthier living which entails minor changes in lifestyle rather than drastic dieting or strenuous exercise. It reveals the way to overcome many of the common chronic problems of our age – backache, tiredness, depression, obesity, anxiety and premature ageing – and build a richer, healthier and happier life. Copies price £2.50 (inclusive of postage and packing) are available only from:

United Health Promotion Ltd,
The Old Rectory,
Lyneham,
Wilts SN15 4PQ

Index

Abelard, Peter 64
Aborigines 40–41, 114
adolescents 40–41, 71
adultery 38
Aeolus (7) 84–5
Africa 50, 101, 104, 108, 146
ageing 69, 77, 125–6, 131–2, 133, 136, 147, 164–5, 185–97
air, fresh 127–8, 129, 210–11
album, aphrodisiac 17, 18
alcohol 142, 147, 151
Ali, Muhammad 51
Allen, Woody 4
anaphrodisiacs 141–2
andosterone 83–4
Andress, Ursula 117
androgyne 152
anger 154–5
anorexia 31
anxiety 3, 30, 52, 111, 180, 181, 183, 184
aphrodisiacs 140–51
Aphrogen 150, 210
appearance 89–97, 181
Appolonius 79
Aristotle 23
armpits 82–3
Arunta tribesmen 110
asceticism 50–51
Association for Marriage and Family 38–9
Astaire, Fred 194
athletes 22, 124, 133–4
attraction 89–97, 125, 181–2
Augustine, St 163
Australia 36, 40–41, 109–10, 114, 134
autonomy 162, 170
autosuggestion 5, 26, 27, 28

babies 13–14, 75, 81
Bali 43

Balzac, Honoré de 15, 63, 166, 191
Bankhead, Tallulah 168
Bantu 62–3
Bath 56
baths
    cold 136–7, 139
    hot 55–6, 57–8, 76
    sauna 161
Baudoin, Charles 5
Bayaderes 103
Baynard, Edward 136
behaviourism 59–60, 157, 163
Bergson, Henri 12
Bernhardt, Sarah 191, 196
Betjeman, Sir John 8
Bettelheim, Bruno 40
Bhagwan Shree Rajneesh 45–6
bidets 86
birds 105, 138
Blake, William 30
Boarmate 84–5
body types 20–21
Bokun, Branko 109
boredom 107–8, 112, 164, 165–70, 191
brains 1, 28–39, 44, 53–4, 57, 58, 60, 81, 107
breasts 14, 70, 93
Brown, Helen Gurney 193, 194–5
Brown-Sequard, Charles 131–2
Bryce-Smith, Derek 148
bull-roarer 109–10
Bunyon, John 71–2, 146
bushmen, Kalahari 75
Butler, Robert 186

camels 61
Cameron, Paul 11
Campbell, Dr 98
cancer 47, 138
cantharides 140, 144–5

Casanova, Giovanni 56, 86, 143, 148
castration myth 182
cats 31, 49
Caucasia 136, 195
celery 151
centenarians 136, 187–8, 193, 195, 197
Chesser, Eustace 115
Chesterton, G.K. 125
children 33, 40–41, 62–3, 75
China 16, 22
Christianity 38, 45, 50
citterns 101
clary 57
clitoris 100, 176
clothes 93–5
cockroaches 80
cold water 136–7, 139
colouring 56
Columbus Factor 164, 165
communication 158–60, 170
concentration 43–8
conditioning 59–60
Condores Effect 134–5
Conteh, John 22
contraception 41–2
Coolidge, Calvin 165
Coué, Emil 5, 26
courtship 62, 64–5, 66, 105
Coward, Noël 41
Crenshaw, Theresa 67
cries 65, 66
crocodiles 98
Culpeper, Nicholas 57
Cutler, Winnifred 85

damiana 150, 151
dancing 103–5, 108
Darwin, Erasmus 23
death rate 194
defence mechanisms 32
deferred gratification 49–50, 51–2, 58
depression 108

de Ropp, Robert 8
desire incongruity 155–6
diary 65–6
Dickens, Charles 93
diet 143–51
Dietrich, Marlene 63
display, genitals 94–5
dogs 53, 59–60, 61, 74, 75
dominance 182–3
Douglas, Jack 94
dreams 29, 39
dress 93–5
drugs
    anaphrodisiac 141–2
    aphrodisiac 140–51
    sedative 61, 142, 151, 175
durian 79

earlobes 71
education, sex 4, 38, 40–42
eggs 143–4
Egypt 23, 35, 46, 54–5, 78, 104, 132
Einstein, Albert 15, 52
Eliot, T.S. 62
Emerson, Ralph Waldo 34
encounter groups 46, 68, 95
endocrinology 132–5
endorphins 54, 67
energy 15, 116–17
Epicureans 52, 54–5, 58
erections, during sleep 131, 190
Erikson, Erik 192
erogenous zones 70
Eros 13, 38
excitement 107–13, 114–15
exercise 121–9, 134–6, 139, 147
exposure 94–5
extroverts 21–2, 26, 118
eyes 90–93, 97
Eysenck, Hans 118, 182–3

faithfulness 53
fantasy 28, 29, 38–9
Farouk, King 140

fatigue 19–27, 107–8, 116, 117, 137, 146–7, 181
fatness 21, 130
fear 109–13, 115
fertility 104–5, 130
films 96, 109, 134, 174–5
Finsen, Neils 138
fish 49, 98, 138
fitness 121–9, 211
Fliess, Wilhelm 79
flutes 101
Flynn, Errol 140
Fonarev, A. 136
food 143–4, 146–51
  refusal 8, 31, 60
  supplement 150, 210
Forman, Simon 123
Forum magazine 14, 94, 161
France 63, 72, 126
Francis of Assisi, St 56, 81
Frank, Ellen 155
Freud, Sigmund 12, 13, 14–15, 16, 32, 153
Friday, Nancy 39, 89, 94–5
frigidity 36, 175
Fromm, Erich 3, 13

garlic 143, 151
gender difference 172–84
Geneva 127
genius 12
geriatrics 136, 147, 188, 190–95
Gillies, Jerry 44
Ginsburg, Sol 20
ginseng 149–50, 151
glands 130–35
Goethe, Johann Wolfgang von 12, 15
Goldberg, B.Z. 24
graffiti 174
Graham, Sylvester 141
Grant, Cary 194
Greeks
  ancient 13, 35, 52
  modern 69
  mythology 13, 38, 57, 152

guilt 30, 37–8, 39, 50

Haleeby, Omar 25, 27
Harlow, Harry 41
Hartogs, Renatus 102
health 19–23, 26, 121–9, 136–9, 189–90, 195, 196–7
heat 55–8
heliotherapy 138
Heller, Joseph 70
Henri IV, King of France 86
Henry VIII, King of England 92
herbs 57, 143, 149–50, 151
Hernip, L. Claudius 193
Hilliard, Marion 19, 117
Hinduism 24, 99, 100, 106
Hippocratic Law of Use 24, 26, 129
Hite, Shere 23, 55, 67, 74, 75–6, 89, 100, 123, 153, 176, 186
Hitler, Adolf 115, 132
holidays 119, 120
hormone replacement therapy 133
hormones 130–39, 150
Horowicz, Alex 135
Hugo, Victor 187
Human Function Curve 107–8, 112–13, 115
Human Sexuality Program 131
humour 116
Hutton, Barbara 54
Huxley, Aldous 59
Huxley, Thomas 17
hygiene 85–8

illness 189–90, 195, 196–7
impotence 179–81, 189–90
India 9, 16, 24, 45–6
indole 79
inhibitions 11–16, 24, 32–9, 175
intimacy 152–3, 158–60
introverts 21–2, 26, 118
ionisers 127–8, 129, 210–11
ISD (inhibited sexual desire) 175
IVA 84, 85, 86

Japan 33, 40, 57, 99–100, 104, 122
Jartoux, Father 149
Jerome, St 38
Jews 16, 50, 78, 143
jogging 124, 134–5, 139
Joplin, Janis 114
Josephus 50
Jung, Carl 13, 162

Kakkar, Vijay 137
Kama Sutra 20, 62, 66, 112
Kaplan, Helen 17, 18, 29, 37–8, 115,
    154, 156, 186
Kegel, Arnold 177
Kellogg, John 141
Kennedy, John F. 23, 168
Kinsey, Alfred 14
Kinsey Institute 2, 20, 127
Kinsey Report 14, 23, 74, 95
kisses 71–2
Koran 93
Kriedman, Ellen 166
Kruif, Paul de 133
Kundalini, goddess 9, 56

Lake, Max 150, 151
Landers, Ann 73
language 35, 36, 39, 64–5, 66
Law of Reversed Effort 5, 10
Leaf, Alexander 195, 197
Leakey, Louis 85
Leonardo da Vinci 179
lesbians 63
Levin, Ronald 146, 149
Levine, Stephen 5–6
libido quotient, questionnaire 208–9
licking 75
Lincoln, Dennis 11
lips 71–2
lobsters 73
Long Beach, California 69–70
longevity 194–5
Louis XVIII, King of France 93
love 152–71, 173
    categories of 13–14

magic 28–9, 46–7, 48, 83, 146
Malinowski, Bronislav 90
manic depression 108
marathon runners 122, 124–5,
    134–5, 147
Marx, Karl 15
Maslow, Abraham 192, 196
masochism 112
massage 57, 58, 76–7
Masters, W.H., and Johnson,
    Virginia 30, 73, 119, 164,
    180–81, 193, 194
masturbation 22, 23, 35, 36, 39, 55,
    100, 122, 176, 191
Maury, Marguerite 57
May, Rollo 153
Mellanby, Edward 138
menstrual cycle 130
Mills, Sir John 167
minerals 146, 148–9, 150–51
monkeys 8, 31, 41, 42, 49, 56, 87,
    107, 130, 162–3, 164
Monroe, Marilyn 23, 70, 181
Montagu, Ashley 75
Monteux, Pierre 187
Morell, Theodor 115
Morris, Desmond 68, 182
moths 80
music 101–3, 104
musk 83–4
Muslims 25, 46

Napoleon Bonaparte 86, 121–2
Nazis 82
New Orleans 104
nostalgia 17, 18
novelty 166–70, 191
NPT (nocturnal penile tumescence)
    190
nudity 33, 35, 36, 39, 50, 94, 95–6,
    97
nutmeg 151
nutrition 143–51

obesity 21, 130

obscenity 35, 36
Ochsner, Alton 126–7
O'Connor, Dagmar 76
octopus 73
oestrogen 135–6, 139, 150, 151
oils, massage 57–8, 76
Olds, James 49
oral sex 36–7, 75, 87
orchids 143
orgasm 4, 25–6, 28, 73, 157, 174, 176, 177
Ortega y Gasset, José 91
Orwell, George 59
Ovid 118
oysters 143, 148

Pachomius, St 82
pain 112, 115
Palmerston, Lord 122
Parr, Thomas 187–8
parties 109
passion 12, 16–18, 39, 154, 178, 196, 197
Pavlov, Ivan 59, 60
PCG (pubococcygeus muscle) 177–8, 183
Pearson, Paul 19–20, 127
Peguan tribesmen 94
penis 179–80
    display 94
    sensitivity 69–70
perfumes 78–88
Perls, Fritz 46, 48
personality 21–2, 26, 118
Peruvia 109
Peter of Spain 31
Petronius 55
pheromones 80–88, 104, 105
phobias 34
pigs 80, 84
Plato 12, 192
play 192
Playboy 112
pleasure 49–58, 163–4, 170–71, 180–81

Polynesian islands 164–5, 187
Pompadour, Madame de 128, 166
Popov, Ivan 149–50
porcupines 80
pornography 35–6, 96, 174–5
positions, coital 122–3, 168
praise 157, 163, 170
prayers 25, 27
projection 32
promiscuity 176–7
prudery 32–9, 41–2
puberty rites 40–41
Puerto Rico 69
Puritans 16, 50, 51, 53, 58, 71–2, 95

Quesnay, Dr 128

rabbits 11, 131
rats, laboratory 49, 54, 75, 164, 194
Ravel, Maurice, Bolero 102
Reeves, Donald 45
Reich, Wilhelm 15, 23
RELATE 210
relationships 152–71, 186–7
religion 9, 12, 16, 24, 25–6, 27, 38, 45, 50, 54
repression 33–9
rest 117, 119, 120
Reuben, David 15
rewards 163, 170–71
Riley, Alan 61
risk 109–13, 115
Rocker, Madam 79
Rollier, A. 138
Rome, ancient 56, 65, 76, 109, 118
roses 57
Royal Bee Jelly 5
Rubin, Zick 91
Rubinstein, Arthur 189
Russell, Bertrand 13, 24
Russell, Michael 82
Russia 28, 45, 100, 126, 136

Sabazius, Father 47
Sacks, Leonard 71

Sacks, Oliver 9
Sade, Marquis de 140
sadism 112
saints 81–2, 146
salad, sensuous 150–51
Sargent, William 110
scents 78–88
Schiavi, Raul 1–2
Schwarzenegger, Arnold 125
seasons 138–9
self-restraint 51–2
Semans, James 119
sensate focusing 180–81, 184
senses 44–7, 60–66
sensitivity, decline 69, 70, 77
sex education 4, 38, 40–42
shame 32–9, 175
sharing 160–61
Sharp, Craig 124
Sheldon, William 20–21
shunamitism 193–4
signalling 56, 60–61
Sinatra, Frank 63, 64
Sirione natives 21
smell, sense of 78–88, 104
smoking 126–7, 129
snake charmers 102, 110
snorting 65, 66
Song of Solomon 78, 79
Soyka, Fred 127
Spanish fly 140, 144–5
spiders 99
statistics 7, 10
Steinback, Manfred 22
Stendhal 175
Stopes, Marie 7, 33–4, 55, 95, 97, 115, 123, 128, 154
stress 109–13, 114, 147, 189
sublimation 14–15, 32
sunbathing 138
suppression 37–8

taboos 33–9, 68, 83, 188
television 118–19
tenderness 63, 64–5, 66, 73–4

tension 23, 53, 111–13, 114
testosterone 115–16, 126, 130–39, 142
Thomas à Becket, St 57
Thrombosis Research Institute 136–7
time
    of day 118, 120
    duration 3, 42–3, 47, 62, 119, 186–7
TMA 85, 86
tokens 47, 48
Tolstoy, Leo 161
tongue 74–5
touch 67–77
    vibrations 98–101, 106
tranquillisers 61, 66, 151
Trobriand islanders 64, 83, 90
Turkey 33, 57, 104, 126

Use, Law of 24–5, 26, 129, 192–3

Van de Velde, Theodoor 56, 67, 73, 99
variety 164–71
vasodilation 55–6
Vatsayana 62
vibrations 98–101, 106
videos 96, 97
Village Voice 92
vitamins 146–8, 150–51
voice 64–5
Voltaire 64
Voronoff, Serge 132–3

Wallace, Wally and Lila 105
warfare 115, 141
warmth 55–8
watama 99–100
West, Mae 89, 91, 119
whales 98–9
Whitman, Walt 96
Williams, Leonard 87, 162–3
witchcraft 28, 46–7, 55
work 116, 118

Xhosa tribe 63

Yerkes-Dodson Law 107–8, 112–13,
   115
ylang-ylang oil 57–8
yoga 16, 42, 123
Young, Brigham 143–4

Zen Buddhists 43, 45
zinc 148
Zolotov, Boris 28, 45
Zoroastrians 25
Zuni Indians 183
Zunin, Leonard 92